MINERALS

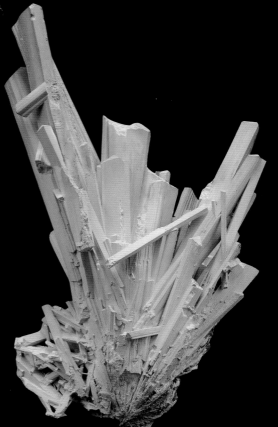

MINERALS

An Illustrated Exploration of the Dynamic World of Minerals and Their Properties

George W. Robinson, Ph.D.
Earth Sciences Division
Canadian Museum of Nature

Photography by
Jeffrey A. Scovil

Mineral specimens from
the collection of the
Canadian Museum of Nature

A Peter N. Nevraumont Book

WEIDENFELD AND NICOLSON

London

First published in Great Britain in 1994 by
Weidenfeld and Nicolson Ltd

Canadian
Museum
of Nature

Musée
canadien
de la nature

Weidenfeld and Nicolson Ltd
The Orion Publishing Group
Orion House
5 Upper St Martin's Lane
London WC2H 9EA

A catalogue record for this book is available from the
British Library.
ISBN 297 83329 4

Printed in Hong Kong by Everbest Printing Company
through Four Colour Imports.

This book was created and produced by
Nevraumont Publishing Company
New York, New York

President: Ann J. Perrini

Book and jacket design: José Conde, Kanazawa City, Japan
Figure illustrations: Jane Axamethy

Contents

PART I   The Earth and Its Minerals 8

chapter 1   Thinking like a Geologist 10

chapter 2   Continents Adrift 15

chapter 3   Minerals 18

chapter 4   The Rock Cycle 22

PART II   Minerals from Molten Rock 28

chapter 5   Crystallization 30

chapter 6   Gems from the Deep 36

chapter 7   Carbonatites: Unusual Rocks
with Unusual Minerals 39

chapter 8   Granitic Pegmatites 42

chapter 9   Agpaitic Pegmatites 56

chapter 10   Summary of Crystallization in Magmas 61

PART III   Minerals and Water 62

chapter 11   Dissolution and Precipitation 64

chapter 12   Hydrothermal Solutions 74

chapter 13   Warming the Rain 76

chapter 14   Beyond Pegmatites 86

chapter 15   The Effect of Tectonism 93

chapter 16   Summary of Water's Role
in Mineral Formation 100

PART IV   Chemical Alteration 102

chapter 17   Equilibrium and Chemical Reactions 104

chapter 18   Drying Out 108

chapter 19   Neutralization Reactions 110

chapter 20   Oxidation-Reduction Reactions   112

chapter 21   Lights, Camera, Action!   117

chapter 22   Which Comes First?   134

chapter 23   Chemical Alteration in Igneous and
Metamorphic Rocks   137

chapter 24   Replacement Deposits   143

chapter 25   Summary of the Chemical Alteration
of Minerals   148

PART V   Recrystallization   150

chapter 26   Heat and Pressure   152

chapter 27   Metamorphism   154

chapter 28   Composition   157

chapter 29   Complex Recrystallization   164

chapter 30   Skarns: Trash or Treasure?   167

chapter 31   Rodingites   175

chapter 32   Summary of Recrystallization   180

PART VI   Summary of Mineral-forming Processes   182

chapter 33   Interaction of Mineral-forming Processes   184

chapter 34   Biogenic Minerals   188

chapter 35   What Have We Learned?   193

Recommended Reading   196

Appendix: Some Additional Minerals and How They Form   197

Index   205

Acknowledgments   208

The Earth

and Its Minerals

chapter one

Thinking like a Geologist

EVEN in childhood I was fascinated by the natural beauty of minerals and intrigued by their seemingly endless diversity of colors and shapes. Finding and studying these treasures of nature became a lifelong obsession. Later I learned that minerals, along with the familiar landscape of mountains, valleys, plains, and oceans that we all too often take for granted, are the natural consequence of billions of years of interaction between dynamic global forces and the materials that make up the planet. What are these forces and materials, and how do they interact? These are the questions that have enticed and will continue to motivate me and other earth scientists for generations to come.

❰ The devastating blasts of Krakatoa or Mount Saint Helens, cataclysmic earthquakes in Italy or California, seasonal avalanches in British Columbia or the Alps, or periodic floods by the Mississippi or Yellow Rivers are continual reminders of the powerful geological forces at work around us. While we mourn our losses, we also perplexedly fail to learn from them and continue to build our homes and cities on major faults and floodplains in defiance of nature. The geological record provides overwhelming evidence that these processes have been and will continue to be operative for millions of years.

❰ The record also shows that numerous dynamic relationships exist between these forces and the materials that make up the Earth. Study has taught me that the same geological forces that cause earthquakes in San Francisco, volcanos in Iceland, or black smokers along the Juan de Fuca ridge beneath the Pacific Ocean, also provide the heat, pressure, and other requirements for making minerals. How do I know what these requirements and materials are? How can I tell that one particular rock or mineral must have formed in an ancient sea and another in an ancient lava flow? By observation and experimentation. Many geological processes can be observed directly. We can watch mountain streams tumble pebbles as they flow downhill to the plains. We can watch a thin crust of salt form along the edge of a mud puddle and cracks develop as the mud dries up. We can watch a volcano erupt. If I encounter a field full of rounded pebbles at the base of a mountain, I don't suspect that the site is an ancient volcano or mud puddle! Common sense and the law of **uniformitarianism** tell me otherwise.

Simply stated, the law of uniformitarianism says that *the present is the key to the past*. Because streams carry pebbles downhill today, they probably did so yesterday, last week, last year, and even a million years ago. Thus, even if there is no flowing water within a hundred kilometers of the pile of pebbles I came upon, logically I can assume that water once flowed here. Although now it may seem merely to state the obvious, when first proposed by James Hutton in 1785 and systematized by Sir Charles Lyell in the 1830s, the law of uniformitarianism not only revolutionized geology but established it as a hypothesis-testing science, based on observation and reasoning. Seeing is believing. Witnessing lava cool before our eyes to form solid rock provides the direct evidence we need to infer a similar origin for ancient lava flows or cinder cones we may encounter elsewhere.

Some things, such as atoms, gamma rays, or the center of the Earth, we can't see, so we must rely on indirect means to visualize their properties. A bat can't see an insect flying past him in the night sky, yet it is able to locate the insect and track its position with sound waves. Similarly, I can't see atoms, yet by diffracting X rays from a tiny crystal of a particular mineral, I am able to learn how its atoms are arranged internally. I can't see, smell, hear, feel, or taste gamma rays, so when I go to the field in search of radioactive minerals, I bring a Geiger counter that can detect them. The fact that many of the Earth's properties and processes, including some of those that characterize and make minerals, cannot be detected or observed directly by human senses does not preclude their existence.

Even though I can't watch most minerals forming, I can predict how and where they might originate. This is not magic. If I know that a certain kind of cake requires baking at 175°C for 45 minutes, then I also know what kind of oven I'll need to make it, and that a refrigerator won't be required. Likewise, if I know the physical and chemical conditions that a mineral needs to form, then I need only look for possible places in the Earth that provide those conditions. If a temperature of 1,500°C is required to synthesize a particular mineral in the laboratory, then looking for that mineral in rocks that form at lower temperatures would make little sense. Sound, straightforward reasoning such as this, taken a step at a time and tested in the field, is the modus operandi of the geologist.

During the last half of the twentieth century, geophysical data from the study of earthquakes and gravity measurements combined with detailed geological mapping of the Earth's surface and ocean floors has provided

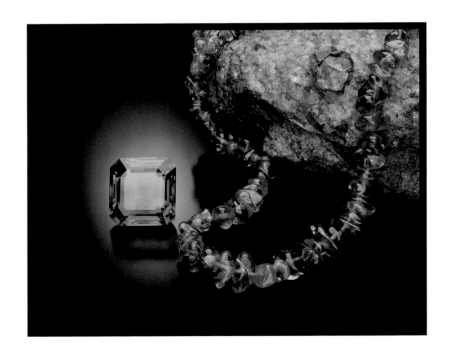

PLATE 1

Nickel-Iron meteorite.
Canyon Diablo, Arizona. 12 x 13 cm.
(Geological Survey of Canada
specimen)

*By studying meteorites such as this one,
geologists are able to learn about the
composition of the Earth and its history.*

PLATE 2

Olivine, variety peridot.
Mogok, Burma (faceted gem,
44.73 ct); San Carlos Indian
Reservation, Arizona (necklace and
specimen, 7 x 8 cm).

*Olivine is a common mineral in the
Earth's mantle and in some meteorites.*

geologists with a whole new concept of the Earth's structure. We now know that the Earth is layered, as an egg is. It has a relatively thin, light, outer **crust** or "shell," which is underlain by a denser **mantle** (the white of the egg), with an even denser "yolk," or **core.** The solid crust on which we live averages 30 to 50 kilometers thick beneath the continents, but only 6 to 8 kilometers thick beneath the oceans. The mantle, which is also solid, is approximately 2,900 kilometers thick, but the core, with a radius of 3,400 kilometers, has a liquid outer portion. Naturally we know more about the crust than we do about any of the other layers, since we can directly sample and analyze the crust. Some direct sampling of mantle rocks also has been possible because pieces of them are sometimes transported to the Earth's surface by volcanic eruptions, but most of what we know about the mantle and core we have learned indirectly from geophysical measurements and the study of meteorites [PLATE 1].

You are probably now asking yourself, What can we possibly learn about the inside of the Earth by studying meteorites from outer space? To answer that question, I will pose another: How did the Earth form in the first place? Of course, no one knows for sure, but the theory upheld by most geologists today suggests that all the planets in our solar system formed by the coalescence and accretion of matter by gravitational attraction. The first particles to combine were probably very small, but as more accumulated, the increase in gravitational attraction due to increased mass attracted larger pieces of matter, such as meteorites and small would-be planets forming at the same time. In fact, the moon probably formed when one such "planet" collided with the Earth, breaking off a section that eventually became the moon.

Ancient meteor-impact craters on the surfaces of both the moon and the Earth are well documented, and meteorites are continually being found all over the Earth. Is it mere coincidence that two of the main minerals found in mantle rocks, olivine [PLATE 2] and pyroxene, are also those found in stony meteorites, or that the observed velocity of seismic waves traveling through the Earth's outer core matches that expected for a molten nickel-iron meteorite containing some silicon? Is it also mere coincidence that the age of the Earth based on the radioactive decay of lead isotopes is the same as that for nickel-iron meteorites: 4.5 billion years?

Much has been learned about the Earth by studying **isotopes.** Isotopes are atoms of the same element with different numbers of neutrons in their nuclei and thus different atomic masses. Some isotopes are unstable and tend to "decay" into more stable forms. To do so they emit energy in the form of radiation at a constant rate. If this rate is known, as it is for many isotopes, then by comparing the amounts of initial isotope and decay products present, we can calculate how much time has passed since the decay began. This process is the basis for the radiometric dating of rocks. In addition, as radioactive isotopes of potassium, uranium, and thorium in the Earth's interior decay into more-stable products, the energy they emit is converted into heat. Inside the Earth, temperature increases with depth, possibly reaching 5,000°C in the core. This increase in temperature with depth is known as the **geothermal**

gradient and averages about 30°C per kilometer in the Earth's crust.

Isotopes are useful geological indicators in other ways as well. Because they have different masses, different isotopes of the same element may partition differently in certain reactions or occur in different ratios in rocks from different parts of the Earth. Increasing knowledge of how various isotopes are distributed throughout the Earth and how they selectively partition from one another during certain chemical reactions is helping geologists interpret many phenomena.

Because heat always flows from hotter areas to cooler ones, within the Earth heat flows from its hot interior to its cooler surface. Much of this heat transfer is accomplished by **convection.** What is convection and how does it work? Here's a simple experiment to try. Prepare an ordinary cup of hot coffee with cream, milk, or whitener and wait a minute or two for motion caused by the stirring to stop. Now, taking care not to cause any motion in the cup, slowly lower a thin, clear ice cube into the coffee. Peer through the ice cube as if it were a glass-bottomed boat and watch what happens. In a few seconds you should see a swirling motion develop beneath the ice cube, which will start to move about, seemingly under its own power. You are observing convection at work. As heat is transferred from the coffee to the ice, it causes the ice to melt. Because the ice water is denser, it sinks toward the bottom of the cup and is replaced by rising, less-dense, hot coffee, which melts more ice, continuing the process. The relative motion set up in the cup by the rising and sinking liquid creates **convection currents** that cause the turbulent flow you see beneath the ice cube. As the convective motion increases, the resulting current is usually strong enough to move the ice cube across the surface of the cup.

A similar situation exists within the Earth. Heat flowing from the core through the mantle to the crust causes convection cells to develop. The crust responds by breaking apart and, like our ice cube, moving about. Of course, the crust moves much more slowly than our ice cube — only a few centimeters a year. This simple concept is the driving force behind what is probably the most important geological theory proposed in modern time: **plate tectonics.**

chapter two

Continents Adrift

THE **plate tectonic** theory proposes that the Earth's crust consists of large **plates** that "float" about its surface because of convective motion through the mantle beneath them. If this sounds a bit far-fetched, don't worry; I was not a believer at first either. After all, for convection to work there must be a flow of materials, and I told you earlier that both the Earth's crust and the mantle beneath it are *solid*. How can a solid flow? The answer lies in *time*, that unique, all-important parameter that separates geology from the other sciences. As humans, we have difficulty believing what we can't see happening. When we toss a stick into a river, we can watch it flow downstream because fluid flow in a river is easily observable within our human time frame and points of reference. A stick thrown onto a glacier, however, even if we stare at it for a month, does not seem to move. But the question remains, did the stick really not move, or did it move so little or so slowly that we couldn't see it happening? ◖ Glaciologists have provided an unequivocal answer. Suspecting that solid ice does indeed flow, glaciologists have proven the point by driving a straight row of posts across the surface of a glacier and marking reference points on land in line with the row at each of its ends. After several months, when the line of posts is surveyed, it is no longer straight, but is bowed outward near its midpoint. With more time, the bow becomes pronounced and visually obvious. The solid ice is flowing, but too slowly for human perception. Given enough time and a slow, steady application of force (in this case, gravity), the solid ice "bends" rather than breaks. Sealing wax, which is also solid, will shatter if given a quick blow by a hammer but will bend, or flow, with a slow, steady application of force, especially if warmed. The same is true of most solid metals. Might not a solid (especially one at 1,200 to 2,500°C), such as the Earth's mantle, also be capable of maintaining a similar slow rate of convective flow?

If you are still a little uncertain about the plausibility of plate tectonics, there is a good deal more tangible evidence supporting the theory. For the plates to "float" they would have to be less dense than the rock beneath them. This is exactly the case. Although the composition of crustal rocks varies widely, in general we find that the continents are **granitic** in composition, while the ocean basins are **basaltic.** Granites contain more lightweight elements, like sodium, aluminum, silicon, and potassium, than do basalts, which contain more of the denser elements calcium, iron, and magnesium. Therefore, the average density of granite is less than that of basalt. Peridotite, which is one of the most common rocks in the upper mantle, has a density greater than that of either granite or basalt. Thus, considering only differences in density, the observed positioning of the continents on top of the oceanic crust, which is on top of an even denser mantle, makes sense.

From deep-sea submersibles scientists have been able to watch submarine volcanic eruptions produce oceanic crustal basalts along midoceanic ridges. Studies of these rocks show that bands of basalts with identical magnetic properties and ages are symmetrically distributed at equal distances on either side of the ridge, with progressively older basalts as one travels farther from the ridge. This compelling evidence for a spreading seafloor is corroborated by calculations indicating that North America and Europe are moving apart at a rate of about one centimeter per year. A quick look at a world map shows that the shapes of opposing continental margins do appear to fit together. Fitting continents back together reveals much more evidence suggesting that they were once joined. Rocks of similar age and structure on opposite sides of the oceans match up, as do rocks containing similar fossil assemblages, glacial features, and magnetic alignment of iron-bearing minerals.

All the evidence points to the conclusion that the continents were formerly joined together and have drifted to their present positions like ships on a sea of moving basaltic plates. But what happens to the continents and plates as they move about? As FIGURE A shows, there are three possibilities: (1) they spread apart, (2) they slide past one another, or (3) one sinks beneath the other. The first scenario produces midoceanic ridges and volcanos, such as those in Iceland. The second produces long fractures along which there is movement, such as the San Andreas **fault** that parallels the California coastline. The frequent earthquakes experienced in California result from the sudden release of energy and fracturing of rock as the plates slide by one another. The third case is exemplified off the east coast of Japan, where a deep-sea trench marks a zone of **subduction.** There a westward-moving oceanic plate **subsides,** or sinks beneath the Asian continent, carrying along with it a good deal of sediment piled on the ocean floor. The deeper the sediment and oceanic crust sink beneath the continent, the hotter they get, until they finally melt. Surrounded by much-denser rock, the less-dense,

Plate Boundaries.

When two plates meet, they spread apart (e.g., East Pacific Rise), slide past one another (e.g., San Andreas Fault), or pass beneath one another (e.g., west coast of South America).

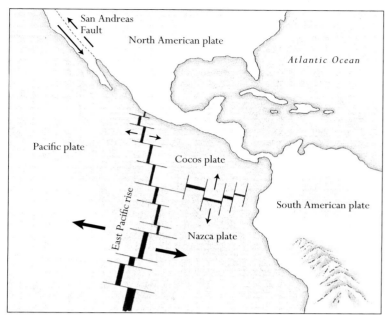

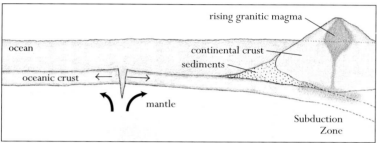

until they finally melt. Surrounded by much-denser rock, the less-dense, molten rock, known as **magma,** follows zones of weakness back toward the surface, where it eventually may erupt as one of Japan's many volcanos.

Because the Earth's crustal plates ferry the continents about its surface, continental collisions also occur. When two continents collide, huge mountain ranges are formed, as crustal rocks are either folded like an accordion or scraped off one continent and piled atop those of the other. The Himalayas formed by such a collision between India and Asia, the Alps by the collision of Africa with Europe.

Why did I say that the plate tectonic theory was probably the greatest geological discovery in modern time? Because it accounts for and ties together so many different geological phenomena. It explains the cause and global distribution of volcanos and earthquakes, the shape of the continents, why we find fossils of ancient marine organisms high and dry on mountaintops, and even why we find certain plants and animals on one continent but not another. It also provides a rational explanation for the evolution and distribution of many minerals, but to understand why, we must first understand what a

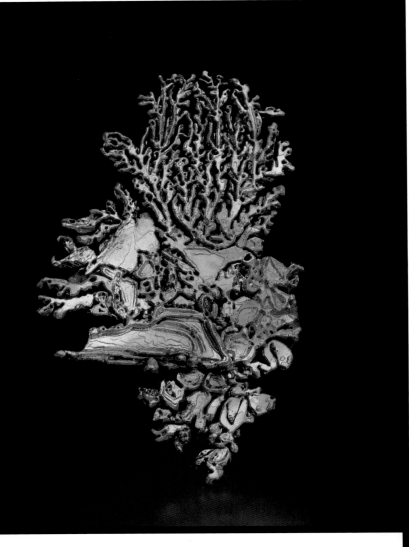

PLATE 3

Gold.

Grass Valley, California. 2 x 3.5 cm.

Gold is one of the few minerals that occurs as a native element. Most minerals are compounds, composed of two or more elements.

PLATE 4

Calcite.

Herja, Transylvania, Romania.
5 x 7 cm.

Calcite is stable over a broad range of temperature and pressure. These spherical aggregates of calcite crystals are only one of its many forms.

chapter three

Minerals

M OST **minerals** are *naturally occurring inorganic solids with defined chemical compositions and crystal structures.* I usually think of them as nature's inorganic chemicals and the Earth as nature's laboratory. A few minerals, such as gold, sulfur, or diamond [PLATES 3, 12, 63, and 135], exist as individual **native elements,** but most are **compounds,** composed of two or more elements chemically bonded together. Like all chemicals, minerals have specific ranges of stability with respect to heat, pressure, acidity, oxidation, and numerous other parameters. If one or more parameters change, some minerals may no longer be stable and will change to form different minerals that are stable in the existing conditions. In that regard minerals are like people. They like to be "comfortable" in their surroundings. No one working in a foundry wants to wear a heavy overcoat, even on a cold winter day, until, of course, it comes time to go outside and walk home. We respond to changes in our environment, and so do minerals. ❰ The plate tectonic model described in Chapter 2 provides many combinations of parameters and the means to change them. For example, at midoceanic ridges there is high heat flow but low pressure; submarine trenches provide little heat but enormous pressure; the collision of continents places dissimilar rocks in contact with one another and provides great lateral pressure; a subducting plate exposes huge areas of rock and sediment to increasing heat and pressure while a rising body of magma created when they melt provides a localized source of heat but not much pressure; and so on. *The wide range of physical and chemical parameters provided by natural geological environments and the availability of specific chemical elements ultimately dictate which minerals will be produced.* ❰ It doesn't matter to a growing crystal of calcite [PLATES 4, 40, 49 and 107] where it forms, as long as its surroundings provide its essential

PLATE 5

Kyanite (blue) **and Staurolite** (brown) **in Mica Schist.**
Monte Campione, Ticino, Switzerland. 6 x 8 cm.

Because they form exclusively under conditions of high heat and pressure, kyanite and staurolite are used by geologists to interpret the history of metamorphic rocks.

PLATE 6

Mesolite on Apophyllite.
Poona, Maharashtra, India.
4 x 6.5 cm.

Sprays of delicate crystals like this mesolite can form only by unimpeded growth into open spaces, such as gas bubble cavities in basaltic lava flows.

ingredients and a stable environment for its growth. Calcite may form equally well in an igneous rock, such as a carbonatite at several hundred degrees Celsius, in a vein in a metamorphic rock like slate at only 200°C, or in a cavity in limestone, a sedimentary rock, at only 20°C. (Igneous, metamorphic, and sedimentary rocks are discussed in Chapter 4.) Calcite has a broad range of stability with respect to heat and pressure. The physicochemical conditions in each of these extremely different geological environments overlap the stability field for calcite, so calcite may occur in any of them. Therefore, by itself, the discovery of a calcite crystal in a rock tells us very little about the geological history of the rock.

Some minerals, however, have more-restricted limits of stability and therefore occupy only a few geological niches. The conditions of high heat and pressure required to form diamonds, for instance, exist only in the Earth's mantle. Stishovite, a rare form of silica (SiO_2), forms only under extremely high pressures, such as realized in rocks that have sustained a meteor impact. Andalusite, sillimanite, and kyanite [PLATES 5 and 112], all of which have the chemical formula Al_2SiO_5, are stable only at specific ranges of pressure and temperature and thus are extremely useful to geologists in deciphering the geological record of rocks that contain them.

Minerals are all around us; the Earth's rocks are composed of them. If minerals are so common, though, why do well-formed crystals seem so rare? Why is it, in spite of hiking over miles of rocks, you have probably never encountered spectacular crystals like those pictured in this book? To understand why this is so, we must look carefully at the underlying mechanism that forms all minerals: **crystallization.** Simply stated, crystallization is the organization of atoms from random into ordered, symmetric arrangements. It is the crystal structure that determines all the properties of a mineral: its shape, color, hardness, and even how it breaks. No two mineral species have the same kind of atoms arranged in the same way.

Most of the magnificent crystals housed in museums and illustrated in this book crystallized in a fluid medium in open spaces. Nonrestrictive surroundings are essential for the growth of large, perfect crystals [PLATE 6]. Time and the availability of essential chemical constituents are also crucial. All other factors equal, large crystals require more time to grow than small ones, but if supplied with the proper ingredients for too long a time, continued growth results in the crystals heading each other off to form a mass of interlocking crystals without well-developed forms. Given all these requirements, it is apparent why large, perfect crystals are scarce in nature: in most geological settings their essential constituents are seldom supplied in the right amount, at the right rate, and at a suitable temperature and pressure with sufficient time or space for them to develop●

PLATE 7

Azurite (blue) **and Malachite** (green).
Bisbee, Arizona. 6 x 8 cm.

Azurite and malachite form as a result of the oxidation of earlier-formed copper-bearing minerals such as chalcopyrite [see PLATE 8].

PLATE 8

Chalcopyrite and Calcite.
Groundhog mine, Vanadium, New Mexico. 4 x 5 cm.

These crystals formed in open space by precipitation from an aqueous solution.

chapter four

The Rock Cycle

ALTHOUGH in general we can say that the genesis of minerals is controlled by crystallization, this statement does not explain the distribution of minerals within the Earth. Such an explanation can be obtained only by considering crystallization in context with geological processes. Only then does it become clear why certain minerals occur where they do. A dynamic balance exists between constructive and destructive forces within the Earth. Vulcanism and continental collisions build up mountains; weathering and erosion tear them down. In the process rocks, and the minerals that comprise them, are recycled. Even a hard, durable rock like granite is not immune to these forces. ❦ The very moment granite is exposed to the Earth's surface, physical and chemical weathering begin to take their toll. Repeated heating and cooling by the sun causes the outermost surface of the rock to expand and contract, physically weakening it until it splits off (of course, the granite could always fall victim to a quarrying operation, which would greatly accelerate the process). As rain falls on the granite, it chemically breaks down its **feldspars,** the most abundant mineral group in the Earth's crust, into clays, releasing grains of quartz and other minerals. These smaller particles are carried from the mountains to the plains by wind, water, or ice, and eventually by rivers to the sea, where they accumulate as layers of sediment. With continued accumulation, sediments compact under pressure to form **sedimentary** rocks, which are eventually carried back toward the continent by the moving plates. ❦ When these rocks reach the continent, some may be carried downward with the plate as it plunges beneath the continent. As they continue their downward journey, increased heat and pressure recrystallizes both the sediments and the

The Rock Cycle.

Rocks are continually recycled by geological processes. Magma crystallizes to make igneous rocks, which are broken down and carried as sediments to the sea by weathering and erosion. The sediments compact to form sedimentary rocks, which recrystallize under heat and pressure, forming metamorphic rocks. Continued heating causes melting, which forms a magma, completing the cycle. Water may be driven from the rocks at various points along the way, producing aqueous solutions.

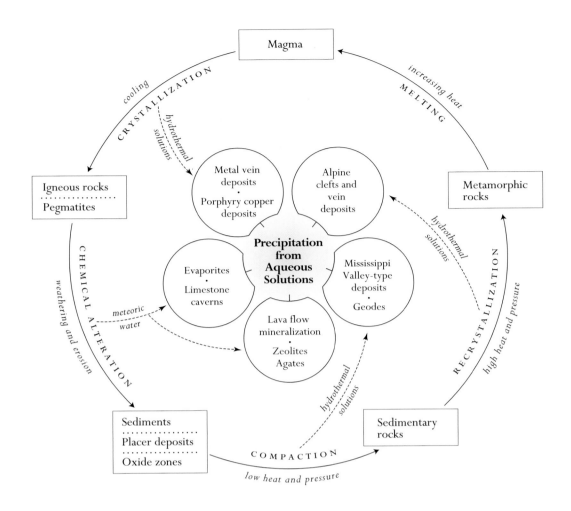

oceanic crust into **metamorphic** rocks. As the rocks descend even deeper, the rising temperature causes them to melt, forming a **magma.** The magma, which is under pressure and is less dense than the surrounding rock, rises upward to form an igneous rock—maybe a granite—as it cools and completes the cycle [FIGURE B].

Of course, there are many shortcuts and side roads that can be taken along the way. For example, igneous rocks may be recrystallized into metamorphic rocks or remelted to form magma without ever having been eroded. Igneous rocks are not the only ones subject to erosion. Sedimentary and metamorphic rocks are equally susceptible and may be recycled directly back to the sea as sediments. Life, too, enters the geological picture. Consider for a moment where each of the calcium atoms in your bones or teeth may have been in the geological past. Perhaps they were once dissolved in an ancient sea, where they were removed by a mollusk and incorporated into its shell as aragonite ($CaCO_3$). When the mollusk died, its shell would have fallen to the sea floor, where it could have been buried for millions of years in the sediment. The aragonite would probably recrystallize into calcite (also $CaCO_3$), while the imprint of the shell remained as a fossil record of former life. As more sediment accumulated, the increased heat and pressure due to burial would have formed limestone. Millions of years later, the processes of uplift and erosion could expose the limestone to the Earth's surface. There it could be discovered and quarried by humans, who might blast it apart and haul it off in a truck to a kiln, where it would be roasted to make lime (CaO) for use as a soil conditioner. Vegetables grown in the conditioned soil could take up some of the calcium, which your body might assimilate when you ate them.

Although these hypothetical calcium atoms in the aragonite, calcite, limestone, and lime represent only a miniscule fraction of the materials that make up the Earth, they illustrate an important point: They may be constituents of very different things depending on the time at which they are observed within an ongoing, natural process of recycling. Eventually, given enough time, the rock cycle is usually completed.

Completing the rock cycle requires that some minerals be created and others destroyed. As FIGURE B shows, the cycle involves four major processes: (1) **crystallization from molten rock,** (2) **precipitation from aqueous solutions,** (3) **chemical alteration of preexisting minerals,** and (4) **recrystallization by heat and pressure.** In the first of these, atoms of different elements are naturally sorted and recombined to form specific minerals as molten rocks cool to form igneous rocks. The minerals that form depend on the composition of the magma and what happens to it as it cools. Minerals such as diamond [see PLATE 12] form deep within the Earth at high temperatures and pressures and therefore are early to crystallize from a magma. Other minerals, such as beryl or topaz [see PLATES 20 and 23], form much later, at lower temperatures and pressures.

The second process centers on the role of water in dissolving, transporting, and recombining various chemical elements to make minerals as different as gold, halite (rock salt), or opals [see PLATES 3, 37, and 41], depending on the source of the water and the kinds of rocks through which it flows. The third process involves specific chemical processes, such as oxidation or changes in acidity, that result in the creation of new minerals like azurite from old ones like chalcopyrite, formed previously by other processes [PLATES 7 and 8]. The fourth process embodies the roles of heat and pressure in restructuring the atoms of previously formed minerals into new arrangements to make various minerals in metamorphic rocks [see PLATE 5]. Some minerals, such as emeralds [see PLATES 20, 120, and 133], may form by more than one process or require combinations of several processes to form. Finally, living organisms also play a role in the creation of some minerals, such as sulfur [see PLATE 135].

The remainder of this book has been organized around the mineral-forming processes that I just described. It is imperative to remember, however, that this scheme of classification is simply one of convenience; it is not inviolable. No definite boundaries have been established between these processes. As with many natural phenomena, often explanations of the genesis of minerals offer more shades of gray than black or white. Many questions have no clear-cut answers. For example, at exactly what point does the heat and pressure

required to compress sediments into sedimentary rocks become enough to
call them metamorphic rocks instead? At what point does recrystallization by
heat and pressure in a semisolid, plastic state leave off and partial melting to
form a magma begin? These points are all arbitrary, and my judgment may
differ from that of other geologists. Where the line is drawn is not important.
What is important is understanding how each process works and its relationships to the others.

Often more than one process is involved in the formation of a particular
mineral. For example, consider the formation of the simple iron-oxide mineral goethite [PLATE 9], which forms the familiar brown rust stains commonly
seen on rocks of all types. The first requirement is a source of iron, such as the
iron sulfide pyrite [see PLATES 65, 78, and 109]. When pyrite comes in contact with groundwater containing dissolved oxygen, it oxidizes into iron sulfate, which further oxidizes in solution and precipitates goethite (i.e., goethite
separates from the solution, since it is insoluble). Operative are at least
two processes: chemical alteration and precipitation from aqueous solution.
Which process is more important to form goethite? The question is irrelevant
because both are essential.

As human beings we tend to see all things relative to our own brief life-
times. Slow change appears to us as no change and therefore goes unnoticed.
Most rocks and minerals change at an imperceptibly slow rate, but they do
change! Thus, the specimens illustrated in this book are a snapshot in time,
subject to transformation by geological processes. Although they may currently reside in human hands, they did not always, nor will they likely forever
remain. To explain the genesis of minerals, a geologist must work like a detec-
tive, interpreting clues left behind by the processes that formed them. He or
she must look for a motive, opportunity, and means to solve the mystery.
In the case of minerals, the motive is their inherent tendency toward chemical
and physical equilibrium with their surroundings. Opportunity is provided
by the diverse geological environments created by plate tectonics and other
geological processes; the means are the four main mineral-forming processes:
crystallization (see Part II), precipitation from aqueous solutions (Part III),
chemical alteration (Part IV), and recrystallization (Part V) ●

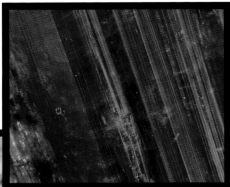

Minerals

from Molten Rock

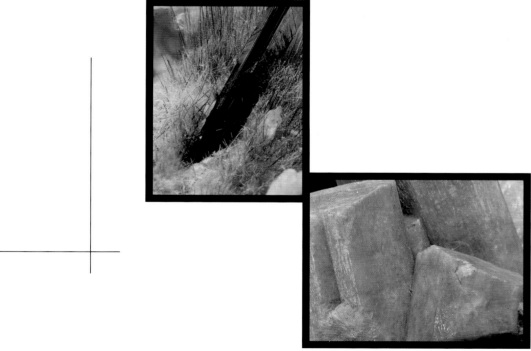

chapter five

Crystallization

FE W things are more spectacular or memorable than a volcano in full eruption. It is also probably the most obvious example of rocks in the making, and the most common answer to the question, how do rocks form? My first encounter with lava was at the site not of an active volcano, but rather an extinct one in northern Arizona. Although the site contained no molten rock, rising steam, sulfurous fumes, intense heat, or raining cinders, I could feel the presence of all these things, for their evidence was all around me. ❦ To my left lay a great, black field of jagged, toffee-surfaced blocks of lava. Here and there large sheets of the black rock had been bulldozed into ridges by the river of molten rock that once flowed beneath them. In the distance to my right was a conical hill of reddish-brown cinders, burning bright in the afternoon sun. Cinders littered the landscape. It was as though all the clinkers I had ever seen on all the railroad lines in my life had been gathered up and scattered across this unfamiliar landscape. It could be nothing else; this was a volcano! Fascinated with the landscape and geological features that until then I had seen only in books and films, I spent an hour taking photographs and walking around, just observing and getting acquainted with this marvelous but alien landscape. One thing I didn't do, though, was look for crystals, for I knew I was not apt to find them here. ❦ A lava field seldom contains large, well-formed crystals of any mineral, since the few minutes to hours that it takes for the molten lava to solidify is usually not enough time for large crystals to form. **Magma** is molten rock; **lava** is magma that comes to the Earth's surface. In general, the faster magma cools, the smaller are the individual crystals that are formed. Often very fine-grained rocks result. Although the rapid cooling of volcanic rocks is not conducive to producing large, well-formed crystals, occasionally we do find such crystals in them. Some of the world's best and largest crystals of leucite occur in lava from the Roccamonfina volcano in the Campania region of Italy, which last erupted in A.D. 276, and large, gem-quality crystals of labradorite are mined from the lavas of extinct volcanos near Plush, Oregon. How do these crystals get so big, if they have so little time to crystallize?

The answer is simple: they do not crystallize at the Earth's surface, even though the rock enclosing them does. Think for a moment of a volcano as simply a safety valve, much like the one on a steam pressure cooker. When the valve on the pressure cooker fails, the drastically lower pressure outside the pot causes not only steam and super-heated water but also bits of partially cooked food from the bottom of the pot to eject. Leucite and labradorite have relatively high melting points, and the crystals had probably already grown to their present size and shape within a subsurface chamber of magma before the volcano erupted. The sudden release of pressure brought about by eruption of the volcano caused the already formed crystals to be carried to the surface along with the lava, just as the solid food is ejected from the bottom of the pressure cooker. Close examination of such crystals typically reveals that their **matrix,** the rock that encloses them, is indeed much finer grained, since it crystallized much more rapidly. Much has been learned about crystallization in magmas by studying such crystals, since their compositions reflect the prevailing chemical conditions at the time of their formation.

In addition to the length of time a magma takes to cool, an equally important and obvious factor that determines what kind of minerals can form is the composition of the starting material. If a particular element is not present in a magma, no mineral containing that element can form when the magma eventually cools. Although some ancient, primordial magmas may well exist in the Earth's mantle or outer core, most magmas probably form by the melting of preexisting rocks. Such melting usually takes place either in the Earth's mantle, where there is sufficient heat, or in the crust above the mantle, where because of their compositions, the rocks have lower overall melting temperatures. For example, as basaltic oceanic crust and sediments are dragged down a subduction zone by tectonic motion, they are heated until they melt. Because the sediments are largely derived from the weathering of granitic rocks from the continental crust, they contain more silicon and aluminum than does the basalt. Thus when they melt, the sediments provide additional silicon and aluminum to the magma, producing magmas more granitic in composition than would the melting of oceanic crust alone. Japan's Mount Fuji probably formed in such a manner. It is composed of andesite, a volcanic rock intermediate in composition between basalt and granite.

The crystallization of magma involves transitions from the liquid to solid state. Relatively unordered atoms or groups of atoms in the liquid must become ordered into solid, crystalline structures as they lose heat energy. But which atoms or elements fit together as the magma cools, and what minerals

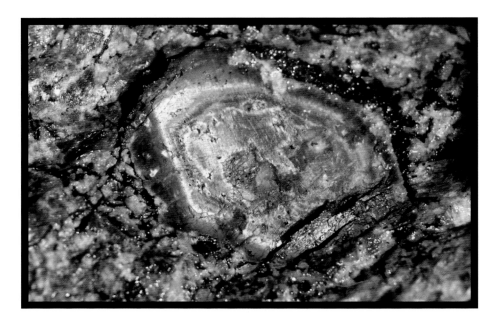

PLATE 10

Labradorite (a plagioclase feldspar).
Nain, Labrador. 6 x 9 cm.
(Photograph by Michael Hamilton,
Geological Survey of Canada)

*Differentiation of magma caused
compositional zoning between calcium and
sodium in this crystal of labradorite.
Because visible light behaves differently as
it passes through the different zones, it
produces this spectrum of colors.*

do they form? One of the first scientists to investigate these questions was Canadian geologist Norman Bowen, who as early as 1922 drew some fundamental conclusions about how minerals crystallize in a cooling magma, many of which still hold. Like many other geologists, Bowen had observed that certain minerals (e.g., olivine, pyroxene, and plagioclase) often form distinct layers of crystals in igneous rocks, but could not explain how and why this was so. Bowen suspected that the removal of these minerals from the magma by crystallization caused the chemical makeup of the remaining magma to change, thus limiting the number of subsequent crystals that could form, but he had no hard evidence, no proof. Since he obviously could not visit a magma chamber many kilometers beneath the Earth's surface to see firsthand how minerals crystallize, Bowen decided to do the next best thing: synthesize a magma chamber in his laboratory, where he could control the composition of the magma as well as its temperature and pressure.

Bowen combined the appropriate amounts of the various chemical constituents of a rock, placed them in a sealed container made from a nonreactive material (such as platinum) that could withstand high temperatures, and melted the ingredients to make a "magma." By controlling the temperature, he could quickly stop the melting, instantly "freezing" the magma into solid "rock." He could then separate and analyze the resulting minerals, along with their glasslike matrix, whose composition represented that of the residual, or remaining "magma." By repeating the experiment at successively lower temperatures, Bowen was able to recreate the paths of crystallization for many minerals.

Beginning with a "magma" of basaltic composition, Bowen noted that minerals with high melting points (such as pyroxene, olivine, spinel and ilmenite) were the first to crystallize. He also observed that as calcium and magnesium were removed from the magma by the crystallization of plagioclase feldspars and olivine, the remaining liquid became progressively enriched in sodium, potassium, and iron. This observation was possible because such compositional trends are recorded in zoned crystals of these minerals, which grow outward from their centers, resembling rings of a tree [PLATE 10]. The cores of the plagioclase crystals contained more calcium than did their rims, which were enriched with sodium. Similarly, olivine and pyroxene crystals showed an outward decrease in magnesium relative to iron content. At lower temperatures minerals such as amphiboles, micas, potassium feldspar, and quartz crystallized.

In addition to quantitatively describing crystallization in a magma for the first time, the qualitative geological implications from Bowen's experiments were staggering. He had shown that many different igneous rocks could evolve from the same initial magma! For the first time geologists understood why basalts like the famous Palisades north of New York City showed accumulations of dense olivine crystals in their lower halves and lighter, calcium-rich plagioclase crystals in their upper portions, or why certain volcanos in Iceland first erupt basaltic lavas, followed by increasingly silicic lavas.

To really appreciate and understand what is going on as minerals crystallize from a magma, we need to look more closely at the atomic level. Because the two most abundant elements in the Earth's crust are silicon and oxygen, the most common kind of magma is a **silicate** magma, which solidifies to form silicate minerals. As the magma cools, silicon and oxygen atoms join together in the shape of a tetrahedron, with one oxygen atom (O) at each of its four corners and a single silicon atom (Si) in its center. Such SiO_4 **tetrahedra** are the building blocks of silicate minerals. In the liquid magma diverse metal atoms, such as potassium, iron, or magnesium, with various sizes and charges are surrounded by networks of SiO_4 tetrahedra, between which they must fit to form crystals. Not all of them make it.

Atoms with unusual sizes and charges do not fit easily into the structures of the minerals that are crystallizing. As various minerals form, rejected atoms are left behind in the residual part of the liquid magma, where they increase in relative concentration. Atoms of any minor chemical elements in the magma will either be incorporated or excluded from a mineral's structure based on how similar they are to the mineral's major constituent atoms [FIGURE C]. It's analogous to tricking a parking meter or vending machine into accepting a metal washer of similar proportions to a coin. The closer the two atoms are in size and charge, the greater the likelihood that one can substitute for the other. For example, the trace element nickel is incorporated early into olivine (magnesium iron silicate) because nickel "feels" like magnesium or iron to a growing olivine crystal. Similarly, elements such as barium and lithium are rejected by early-forming minerals but are incorporated into later-forming potassium-dominant feldspars or micas whose structures are better suited to accommodate them.

By the end of the crystallization sequence, the residual liquid no longer resembles the original magma at all. It is greatly enriched with water, fluorine,

ACCEPTED ATOMS

Silicon (Si^{4+})

Magnesium (Mg^{2+})

Iron (Fe^{2+})

Oxygen (O^{2-})

REJECTED ATOMS

Potassium (K^+)

Beryllium (Be^{2+})

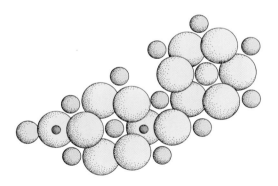

FIGURE C

The Crystallization of Olivine.

Composed of magnesium, silicon, and oxygen atoms, olivine is one of the first minerals to crystallize as a silicate magma cools. Often olivine also contains iron, since iron atoms are similar in size and charge to magnesium atoms. Other elements, such as potassium or beryllium, do not easily fit into the structure of olivine, and therefore remain in the magma to form different minerals later at lower temperatures.

Magmatic Processes.

*Many things can happen to a magma
when it intrudes a rock. Pieces of the
intruded rock may break off and be
assimilated by the magma. Volatile
components may diffuse into or out of
the magma. Other chemical components,
soluble at higher temperatures, may even
segregate and form a separate magma.
All these processes change the composition
of the magma and influence which
minerals form.*

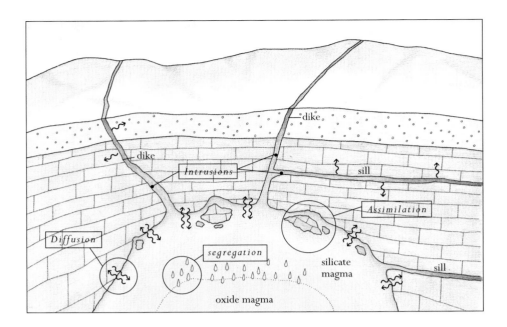

and other volatile components, along with other "incompatible" elements that
were present in the original melt. Elements such as boron, beryllium, niobium,
tantalum, zirconium, tin, tungsten, thorium, or uranium, whose atoms are of
unusual size or charge, become concentrated. The residual melt is made up of
these "rejects." A colleague describes the crystallization of minerals as "the law
of constant rejection" (although I'm sure his students probably think he's refer-
ring to dating). The further crystallization of this leftover, water-rich magma
full of the "rejects" may result in deposits of many strategically important metals, and when conditions are favorable, produces many of the large, perfect
crystals of exotic mineral species pictured in this book.

The progressive change in the composition of a magma due to the removal
of various constituents is known as **differentiation.** Hundreds of geologists
since Bowen have continued to study differentiation by recreating magma cham-
bers in their laboratories using sophisticated high-temperature and pressure-
confining cells called bombs. Occasionally, one lives up to its name! Although
many principles of differentiation have been eloquently refined since the days of
Bowen, many questions remain unanswered. Reproducing in the laboratory the
conditions thought to exist in a natural magma chamber is certainly very difficult, but maintaining them for geological time is impossible. Some "slow" reactions we will never be able to observe. Furthermore, in natural systems there
are far too many variables to anticipate or to control in a simulated environment; too many things can go wrong. We seldom observe predicted differentiation going to completion because usually something happens to interrupt it.
What might those interruptions be? Let's go back to the kitchen and see.

When I make a pot of vegetable-beef soup, I can deviate a great deal from
the basic recipe in my cookbook and still end up with a vegetable-beef soup. I
may even wish to convert my soup to stew by adding some flour or cornstarch,
and I may have to adjust the heat, since each time I add new ingredients, I am
really creating a new soup, with a new composition and new properties. Like

PLATE II

Magnetite in Carbonatite.
Oka, Quebec. 4.5 x 6 cm.

This unusual texture is probably due to the segregation of two liquids that could not dissolve completely in one another during the cooling of a carbonate-rich magma.

Bowen, who controlled the composition and temperature of his laboratory "magmas," I can control the ingredients and temperature of my soup, but in the natural world, no one can be in control. When magma intrudes rock, pieces of the rock may break off and mix with it, adding new ingredients to the "soup." Known as **assimilation** [FIGURE D], this process can have profound physical and chemical effects on the magma. Not only are new chemical components added to the magma from the rocks assimilated, but other elements are removed from the magma because various minerals are forced to crystallize as heat is lost to the colder, assimilated rocks.

Diffusion of materials between a magma and the rock that surrounds it also may occur, changing the compositions of both. To understand this process, pretend you came into my house as I was cooking my soup. Chances are you could smell the onions, spices, and other volatile ingredients in the air and could deduce what my supper was going to be. Were it not for diffusion, the uniform spreading out of molecules from areas of higher concentration (the pot) to areas of lower concentration (the air in the house), this would not be possible. Diffusion may occur in either direction. When a rock is intruded by a magma, elements such as lithium or beryllium, which exist in higher concentrations in the magma than in the rocks surrounding it, may diffuse into the rock.

Even without assimilation or diffusion, as a magma differentiates, changes in its composition and temperature may result from the **segregation** of two or more immiscible fluids [see FIGURE D]. Like a bottle of well-shaken salad dressing—which eventually separates into oil, vinegar, and spices—oxide-, sulfide-, or carbonate-dominant magmas may segregate, or "unmix," from an originally silicate-dominant magma [PLATE II]. Each of the segregated magmas may differentiate further and produce completely different minerals. Because of differences in density, heavy minerals such as chromite, ilmenite, platinum and various metal-sulfide species may settle out and concentrate to form deposits of mineable size •

chapter six

Gems from the Deep

NOW that we have explored generally how minerals crystallize from molten rock, it's time to turn our attention to some specific minerals that formed that way, one of the most popular of which is diamond [PLATE 12]. (So far, only Superman has succeeded in making it from coal!) Traditionally, primary diamond occurrences have been limited to the relatively uncommon, though widely distributed, igneous rock, kimberlite (named for Kimberley, South Africa, where diamonds have been mined for over a century). More recently, diamonds have been discovered in another kind of igneous rock, lamproite, and they are currently being mined from at least one such deposit at Argyle, in Western Australia. Both kimberlite and lamproite are thought to have formed 150 to 200 kilometers beneath the Earth's surface, in the upper mantle, where the extremely high temperature and pressure required to produce diamonds exist. For years it was assumed that diamonds must somehow form in kimberlitic or lamproitic magmas. Recent studies, however, have produced overwhelming evidence to the contrary, proving that the diamonds did not form in either of these rock types! ❦ Although we cannot directly determine the age of diamonds themselves with present technology, we can date other minerals (e.g., garnet) that crystallize from the magma at the same time and are trapped as inclusions in the diamonds. Relatively new microchemical techniques capable of detecting minute quantities of certain radioactive isotopes that are sometimes present in garnets have shown that garnet inclusions in diamonds from Kimberley, South Africa (and by analogy, the diamonds themselves), are as much as 3.2 billion years older than the kimberlite in which they occur. No way could these diamonds have crystallized from the same magma as the

PLATE 12

Diamond crystal in Kimberlite.
Mir Pipe, Yakut, Russia. 6 x 8 mm.

Although embedded in kimberlite, this diamond crystal did not originally form in this rock.

kimberlite! An intrusion of kimberlite (or lamproite) simply provides a convenient shuttle service to transport the diamonds, which it incorporates as inclusions along the way, to the Earth's surface. Diamonds probably form in the mantle, as huge slabs of basaltic oceanic crust are carried down zones of subduction at continental margins in accordance with the model of plate tectonics. As the basalt slabs are forced beneath the continental crust, they are subjected to a tremendous change in temperature and pressure, which transforms them into a rock known as eclogite. The wide variation in carbon isotopes of diamonds from eclogites suggests that the carbon that constitutes them may be derived from carbonate-rich sediments and/or organic material dragged downward along with the oceanic crust. Maybe Superman is onto something after all!

Placer deposits are another well-known source of diamonds, although the diamonds clearly do not form in them. Placer mining employs water to separate gems or precious metals from gravels; perhaps the most familiar example is gold panning. Placer deposits result from weathering and erosion. (The diamond deposits around Diamantina, Minas Gerais, Brazil, near the Orange River in South Africa, and in the famous Golconda mines in Maharashtra, India, are all of this type.) At the Earth's surface, peridotites and kimberlites are broken down into soils by weathering. In the process, diamonds and other resistant minerals, such as pyrope garnet and chrominum-rich minerals, that may accompany them are freed. Because these minerals are relatively hard and similar in density to diamonds, they are transported with diamonds by erosion, and are useful as prospecting indicators. The diamonds that have been recovered from placer deposits are some of the world's finest, which according to Darwin's theory of natural selection we might predict, since only the fittest survive the harsh processes of weathering and erosion.

Many other gem minerals form by crystallization from magma. Like diamond, most have high melting points and relatively simple chemical compositions. A few of the more common gems that form this way are some rubies and sapphires, spinel, zircon, pyrope garnet, olivine (peridot), and chrome diopside [PLATE 13]. Also like diamonds, many of these minerals occur as distinct inclusions in volcanic rocks, and many have subsequently been concentrated or relocated in placer deposits by weathering and erosion●

chapter seven

Carbonatites: Unusual Rocks with

Unusual Minerals

CARBONATITES, a group of unusual igneous rocks, often host rare minerals. No one knows exactly how carbonatites form, but most geologists believe they are derived from the mantle. As their name implies, carbonatites are composed chiefly of carbonate minerals, most commonly calcite. This composition sets carbonatites apart from all other igneous rocks, which are composed predominantly of silicate minerals. Another distinguishing feature of carbonatites is that they normally contain relatively high concentrations of strontium, niobium, thorium, and rare earth elements. These elements may combine to form such exotic species as pyrochlore [PLATE 14] and other minerals of interest to both scientists and collectors because of their unusual compositions and rarity. Many are also of economic importance. Niobium is used in manufacturing alloys with great strength and resistance to high temperatures, and both niobium and the rare earth elements are becoming increasingly important in the superconductor industry. Other more-common elements, such as iron, titanium, and phosphorus, have also been mined from carbonatites in the form of magnetite, rutile, and apatite. ❰ Minerals that form in carbonatite magmas share similar crystallization trends with those that form in other magmas. Species with high melting points, such as magnetite and rutile, form before those with lower ones, such as amphiboles or micas. Because carbonatite magmas also may differentiate, certain minerals crystallizing from them may show compositional changes with time, just as pyroxene and olivine do in basalts [see Chapter 5]. Although the actors may have changed, the story line has not. ❰ One of the most mineralogically interesting carbonatite occurrences I have ever visited was exposed by the Francon quarry on Montreal

PLATE 14

Pyrochlore crystals in Calcite.
Veshnovorgorsk, Chelyabinsk Oblast,
Russia. 5 x 6 cm.

*Pyrochlore forms in carbonatite magmas
rich in niobium, an element important to
our space-age technology.*

PLATE 15

Weloganite.
Francon quarry, Montreal, Quebec.
4.5-cm crystal.

*Named for W. E. Logan, founder of
Canada's Geological Survey and National
Museum, weloganite is known to exist in
only a few deposits formed by
differentiation of alkalic magmas.*

Island, Quebec. Unlike most carbonatites, those in the Francon quarry occur as **sills.** A sill is a flat, sheetlike intrusion of igneous rock that is parallel to the layers of the intruded rock. The Palisades sill north of New York City is a famous example. Because the carbonatites in the Francon quarry formed sills, when the magma intruded the enclosing rock (in this case a limestone), the magma was quickly chilled and solidified at its upper and lower contacts, effectively sealing it off from its surroundings. In the process, however, volatile components such as water, fluorine and carbon dioxide were sealed in with the magma, enabling differentiation to evolve an unusual, late-stage fluid, enriched in volatiles and rare elements, by the "law of constant rejection." Differentiation in most carbonatites never reaches such a late stage. Lighter than the surrounding magma, "bubbles" of this fluid segregated and rose toward the top of the sill, where they accumulated to form a layer of "pockets," or cavities. The pockets range in size from a few centimeters to nearly half a meter across, and almost all are lined with exotic, well-crystallized minerals, ten of which have been identified as species new to science. At present the quarry is being reclaimed as a landfill site, but the proliferation of specimens it provided in its twenty years of production will be admired and studied for generations.

Probably the most famous mineral found at the Francon quarry is the rare species weloganite [PLATE 15]. Not until we examine weloganite's composition, however, does it become apparent why it formed in this unusual carbonatite. Chemically, weloganite is a hydrated (i.e., it contains water) strontium-sodium-zirconium carbonate. In general, minerals containing water are stable only at relatively low temperatures (around 200°C or less), which are achieved only during the last stages of magmatic differentiation. Weloganite also contains strontium and zirconium, two elements whose atoms are of unusual size and charge and therefore do not fit easily into most crystal structures. Thus, these elements are relegated to forming what minerals they can — in this case, weloganite — at the latest possible time in the crystallization sequence ●

PLATE 16

Euclase.

Minas Novas, Minas Gerais, Brazil.
3 x 4 cm.

*Because beryllium atoms are so small, they
are rejected by early-formed minerals in
granitic magmas and are left to form
exotic minerals, such as this euclase, near
the end of the differentiation process.*

PLATE 17

Columbite and Albite.

Governador Valadares, Minas Gerais,
Brazil. 1.5 x 2 cm crystal.

*Like so many minerals found in granitic
pegmatites, columbite contains an element
of unusual size and charge: niobium.
Columbite is found in only certain granitic
pegmatites, but albite is common in most.*

chapter eight

Granitic Pegmatites

PEGMATITES are very coarse-grained, intrusive igneous rocks that are more or less equivalent in gross composition to their parent rocks—somewhat like a tossed salad as compared to vegetable juice. For example, granite is an igneous rock composed largely of feldspar, quartz, and mica; so is **granitic pegmatite.** The main difference between these two rocks is the size of the individual crystals of feldspar, quartz, and mica that comprise them. In granite, the size of the grains (crystals) of these minerals averages 1 to 5 millimeters, but in granitic pegmatites, grains 1 to 5 centimeters in diameter are common, if not small. Granitic pegmatites, which are derived from a magma with the composition of granite, are by far the most common kind of pegmatite—so common that unless specified otherwise, the word "pegmatite" alone has come to imply "granitic pegmatite." Don't forget, though, that almost any kind of magma can produce a pegmatite. ❦ Many pegmatites form tabular, intrusive structures known as **dikes** [see FIGURE D]. Dikes and sills form in the same way: by intrusion of magma. The difference is in their structural relationship to the rock that they intrude. Dikes cut across the layers of rock they intrude; sills lie parallel to them. Not all pegmatites form dikes. Germany's famous Hagendorf South pegmatite, for example, is turnip-shaped. Some pegmatites form small, localized segregations within the host rock, which often contain a central open void, or crystal pocket. Known as **miarolitic cavities,** these pockets probably form by the separation and accumulation of volatile components in the magma during the last stages of crystallization. In general, miarolitic cavities occur in pegmatites that form at relatively shallow depths in the Earth's crust because the higher pressure associated with greater

PLATE 18

Red Beryl.
Wah Wah Mountains, Utah.
1 x 1.2 cm.

In spite of numerous occurrences of topaz rhyolites worldwide, crystals of red beryl have been found in only one or two such deposits in Utah, suggesting that the conditions for their formation are not easily duplicated.

PLATE 19

Spessartine in Rhyolite.
Ely, Nevada. 1-cm crystals.

Spessartine is one of the most common species of garnet in both topaz rhyolites and granitic pegmatites, since both these rocks originate from magmas with similar compositions.

depths is not conducive to the segregation and accumulation of volatiles. This pressure inhibits the formation of miarolitic cavities in the same way that standing on bread dough would prevent it from rising.

Pockets similar to miarolitic cavities occur in pegmatite dikes when the water content of the magmatic fluid is too high to remain "dissolved" in the magma. The excess water separates out along with some of the rare elements, forming pockets—the source of many gem crystals and fine mineral specimens. Ironically, the very water that is necessary to create these pockets can also cause their destruction. At higher temperatures water exists as steam, and if its vapor pressure increases until it exceeds the confining pressure imposed by the surroundings, an explosion occurs, just as it would in a steam boiler tank. The resulting physical and thermal shock causes earlier-formed crystals in the pocket to shatter. That's why in most gem pockets the gem crystals are found detached from the walls or as shards of broken and healed crystals. If the gem pocket did not rupture, however, it would likely stew in its own juices and engulf its contents, since many of the earlier-formed gem crystals would not be stable under such chemical conditions and would dissolve. Like predator and prey, that which destroys also ensures survival.

In spite of voluminous research on pegmatites, geologists still are not sure why they come about and why their individual mineral grains develop such large crystals. In rare cases these crystals may attain lengths up to 15 meters, as demonstrated by spodumene crystals at the Etta pegmatite in the Black Hills of South Dakota, or the 10-meter-long crystal of beryl found in 1950 at the Bumpus quarry, near Bethel, Maine. Extremely slow cooling rates, optimum conditions for diffusion, and the presence of water and various fluxing agents (chemical components that promote crystal growth) have all been proposed as mechanisms to promote crystal growth. Probably all these factors play roles of varying importance depending on the situation.

Because they form late in the crystallization of a magma, pegmatites frequently contain minor concentrations of unusual minerals. By the time a granitic magma differentiates to the pegmatite stage, the residual melt is typically enriched with water, fluorine, and other volatile components, as well as uncommon elements such as boron, lithium, beryllium, niobium, tantalum, and others, provided they were present in the original magma. It is these elements that are responsible for such exotic minerals as euclase or columbite [PLATES 16 and 17], in addition to a number of gem minerals. Occasionally a magma that might form a granitic pegmatite beneath the Earth's surface finds its way above ground and erupts as the volcanic rock, rhyolite. One variety, topaz rhyolites, are very rich in fluorine, and in addition to topaz may host unusual minerals such as bixbyite, red beryl, and spessartine garnet [PLATES 18 and 19]. The occurrence of these minerals in structurally "late" features such as cavities and open spaces along fractures suggests that the fluorine, manganese, beryllium, and other elements required for their growth accumulated in a late-stage fluid that probably existed as a vapor when the

PLATE 20

Beryl.
Minas Gerais, Brazil (golden, 4 cm; aquamarine, 7 cm); Jos, Nigeria (emerald, 5 cm).

The colors in these three gem varieties of beryl are regulated by very minor amounts of impurity elements: iron in the case of aquamarine and golden beryl; chromium or vanadium in the case of emerald.

PLATE 22

Chrysoberyl.
Espírito Santo, Brazil. Gem, 10.77 ct; crystal, 2.5 x 4 cm.

This unusual star-shaped crystal is the result of twinning, a process in which two or more single crystals grow together in a symmetrical relationship.

PLATE 21 *(opposite)*

Elbaite.
Tourmaline Queen mine, Pala, California. 10-cm crystals.

The dramatic change in color in these crystals of elbaite, a lithium-rich tourmaline, is probably due to a change in the manganese and iron concentrations in the fluid in which it grew.

PLATE 23

Topaz.
Kleine Spitzkoppe, Namibia (crystal,
4 x 4 cm); Mason County, Texas
(gem, 48.35 ct).

*Topaz is one of many gem minerals mined
from granitic pegmatites throughout the
world.*

PLATE 24

Almandine.
Hedgehog Hill, Peru, Maine.
6 x 9 cm.

*Perhaps the most common species of garnet
in granitic rocks, almandine crystals such
as this one have been found in many of
New England's pegmatites.*

minerals crystallized from it because of the rapid decrease in pressure encountered at the Earth's surface.

Not all rhyolites or granitic pegmatites contain exotic minerals. Like granites, which consist largely of quartz, feldspars, and mica, some granitic pegmatites are mineralogically simple. The type of pegmatite that forms depends largely on two factors: the chemical makeup of the original magma and the depth at which it forms. In general, pegmatites that are derived from granites already enriched in boron, lithium, and rare elements and that form at medium to shallow depths in the Earth's crust show the most complex and diverse assemblages of minerals.

As a genetic group, no other type of deposit is known to host a more varied array of important gem minerals than do the granitic pegmatites. They are the primary source of aquamarine, tourmaline, chrysoberyl, and topaz, as well as significant producers of almandine and spessartine garnets, some emeralds, and a long list of less familiar gems [PLATES 20 to 24]. The range of colors, clarity, superior hardness, and relatively high refractive indices of these minerals make them ideal gemstones. Some are varieties of the same mineral species. For example, aquamarine, emerald, heliodore, and morganite are each a differently colored variety of the species beryl [see PLATE 20]. Similarly, kunzite and hiddenite are the lavender and green varieties of the species spodumene.

Individual gems or crystals of some of these minerals may show two or more zones of different colors. In the tourmaline species elbaite [see PLATE 21], one color variant occurs with sufficient regularity to have earned the name "watermelon" tourmaline because of its pink interior and green rim. The ability of certain elements to induce color in minerals has earned them the name **chromophores.** The color in all these gem minerals is caused by extremely *minor* amounts of contaminant chromophores such as iron, manganese, chromium, vanadium, or copper, but it is their *major* element constituents that define the species. The dramatic color zonation exhibited by multicolored and watermelon tourmaline reflects changes in the availability of chromophores to the growing crystal. Color zonation may be due to crystal structural preferences for specific chromophores or may indicate an abrupt change in fluid composition, as might occur during pocket rupture.

Granitic pegmatites have become so well known for their exotic and gem minerals that we too often forget that they also produce some of the world's finest examples of their primary constituents: feldspars, quartz, and micas. Were it not for the industrial demands for these more common minerals, most pegmatite deposits would never have been worked! Most granitic pegmatites host two different kinds of feldspars: the potassium-rich species, orthoclase or microcline [PLATE 25], and the sodium-rich species, albite [PLATE 26].

Every known color variety of quartz has been found in granitic pegmatites. One of the most common is smoky quartz [PLATE 27]. Granites in general, and their pegmatites in particular, contain above-average concentrations of the

PLATE 25

Microcline, variety amazonite.
Pikes Peak, Colorado. 7 x 12 cm.

*The Pikes Peak area of Colorado is famous
for its crystals of amazonite, which form in
open voids in granite, known as miarolitic
cavities.*

PLATE 26

Albite (white) **and Microcline**
(beige).
Minas Gerais, Brazil. 15 x 18 cm.

*Together these two feldspars constitute
much of the volume of all granitic
pegmatites.*

PLATE 27 *(opposite)*

Smoky Quartz and Albite.
Middle Moat Mountain, North
Conway, New Hampshire. 4 x 4 cm.

*These crystals of smoky quartz and albite
were collected from a miarolitic cavity in
granite by the author, circa 1966.*

PLATE 28

Rose Quartz.
Minas Gerais, Brazil. 8 x 14 cm.

Unlike other varieties of quartz, rose quartz crystals such as these are found exclusively in granitic pegmatites.

PLATE 29

Muscovite.
Conselheiro Penã, Minas Gerais, Brazil. 7 x 13 cm.

Because of the abundance of potassium, aluminum, and silicon in granitic magmas, muscovite is one of the most common micas produced when the magma cools to form a granitic pegmatite.

PLATE 30 *(opposite)*

Molybdenite.
Malartic, Quebec. 1.5 x 2 cm.

Sulfide minerals such as this crystal of molybdenite are usually found in hydrothermal vein deposits rather than in pegmatites.

PLATE 3 I

Triphylite.
Smith mine, Newport, New
Hampshire. 2.5-cm crystal.

*Well-formed crystals of triphylite such as
this one are rarely preserved in granitic
pegmatites because they are chemically
attacked by late-stage, residual fluids near
the end of a pegmatite's crystallization
sequence.*

PLATE 3 2

Monazite.
Joaquim Felicio, Minas Gerais, Brazil.
2.5 x 3 cm.

*Monazite, a phosphate of cerium, often
contains uranium, thorium and other rare
elements typical of granitic pegmatites.*

radioactive elements uranium and thorium, as well as some radioactive potassium in their feldspars and micas. With time, the radiation emitted from these elements causes quartz that contains trace amounts of aluminum substituting for some of its silicon atoms to appear a dark, smoky color. Rose quartz [PLATE 28] is also common and sometimes extremely abundant in granitic pegmatites. After much investigation the prevailing theory is that its pink color is due to the presence of titanium or manganese substituting for silicon. Less commonly, citrine quartz and amethyst are found in some pegmatites.

Only three species of mica are common in granitic pegmatites: muscovite [PLATE 29], biotite, and to a lesser extent lepidolite, which is restricted to lithium-bearing pegmatites, and often accompanied by the lithium-rich tourmaline, elbaite. Biotite and muscovite are more widespread. Unlike muscovite, biotite seldom forms pocket-type crystals because in most pegmatites biotite crystallizes before the pocket-forming stage begins.

Many other minerals are found in individual granitic pegmatites. Some are common, others exceedingly rare. Occasionally unexpected minerals appear in granitic pegmatites. For example, excellent crystals of molybdenite occur in a pegmatite near Malartic, Quebec [PLATE 30], and well-formed silicic edenite crystals occur in the McLear pegmatite near DeKalb Junction, New York. The chemical constituents required to form such minerals can usually be traced to the source rocks of the magma or to assimilated rocks. Some pegmatites host significant quantities of phosphate minerals. The most common is fluorapatite, although some pegmatites contain large pods of lithium-, manganese-, or iron-rich phosphates such as amblygonite, lithiophilite, or triphylite [PLATE 31]. Less-common phosphates, such as xenotime or monazite [PLATE 32], may be locally abundant in pegmatites, as are simple oxide minerals such as rutile or cassiterite (tin oxide). Some pegmatites in Western Australia have even been commercially worked for tin ●

chapter nine

Agpaitic Pegmatites

NAMED for Agpat, a locality in southern Greenland, **agpaites** are feldspar-rich igneous rocks with unusually high concentrations of alkali metals, especially sodium, and low concentrations of aluminum and silica. Agpaites are often found near carbonatites. In addition to feldspars, the common rock-forming minerals in agpaites reflect their unusual chemistry and often include sodium-rich species such as nepheline and sodalite. Differentiation of agpaitic magma generally parallels that of other magmas, with pyroxenes crystallizing before amphiboles, which crystallize before micas. Because of the high alkali metal content of the magma, however, the specific minerals formed are different. The main pyroxene mineral is the sodium-rich species aegirine [PLATE 33], and the sodium-rich amphibole tends to be arfvedsonite. ❡ By the time an agpaitic magma differentiates to a pegmatite stage, it has usually become enriched with zirconium, as well as titanium, niobium, thorium, strontium, barium, beryllium, and rare earth elements because these elements do not fit easily into the structures of the early-formed minerals. Because of their unusual chemistry, agpaitic pegmatites host a long list of uncommon to exceedingly rare minerals, some of which (e.g., eudialyte) may be potentially useful as a source of zirconium. Other rare species in these rocks constitute a veritable treasure trove for scientists and collectors. Intrusive complexes of agpaitic rocks are known around the world, but the most famous are those in Russia's Kola Peninsula, in southern Greenland, in Norway, and at Mont Saint-Hilaire in Quebec. ❡ Conditions of formation for several species common in agpaitic pegmatites must be similar, for their mutual presence and relative orders of formation in the crystallization sequence appear similar even in widely

PLATE 33

Aegirine.
Mont Saint-Hilaire, Quebec.
4 x 4.5 cm.

*This species of pyroxene contains abundant
sodium, as might be expected for a mineral
commonly found in alkalic rocks.*

separated occurrences. For example, when collecting at the famous locality of
Narssârssuk in southern Greenland, I was struck by similarities between many of
the minerals I found there and those I had seen at Mont Saint-Hilaire, Quebec,
which I had visited only a few weeks earlier. At both localities well-formed crystals of similar minerals occur in miarolitic cavities in a gray, nepheline-bearing
rock. Frequently the rock coarsens and displays a pegmatitic texture around the
cavities. Since crystallization in these cavities must proceed from the outside in,
the earliest minerals form at the outer margins of the pockets and the last to
crystallize fill the pocket interiors. The major constituents of the pegmatite band
surrounding the pocket at both localities are typically potassium feldspar and
aegirine, showing that these were the first minerals to crystallize.

Well-formed crystals of eudialyte are also among the early-formed minerals,
and the main plagioclase feldspar at each locality is the sodium-dominant species
albite, most of which crystallized after the potassium feldspar. I was surprised to
find transparent, pale pink albite forming overgrowths on the potassium feldspar
at Narssârssuk, since I had previously seen that association on only a few specimens from Mont Saint-Hilaire. These minerals were succeeded by a series of
uncommon minerals, such as elpidite [PLATE 36], that are rich in zirconium and
other elements whose atoms are of unusual sizes or charges. Among the last
minerals to form in these pockets were natrolite, quartz, and various carbonate
minerals, such as synchysite [PLATE 35] and calcite. Although my observation of
these trends in crystallization at both Narssârssuk and Mont Saint-Hilaire is

PLATE 35

Synchysite and Albite.
Narssârssuk, Greenland.
2.5 x 4.5 cm.

*Minerals like synchysite that contain
rare earth elements, carbonate, fluorine, or
other volatiles are among the last to
crystallize from a magmatic fluid. Albite
usually forms earlier.*

PLATE 36

Elpidite.
Mont Saint-Hilaire, Quebec.
10 x 14 cm.

*To date, the quarries at Mont Saint-
Hilaire have produced the world's finest
specimens of this rare sodium-zirconium-
silicate mineral.*

PLATE 34

Serandite (orange) **and Analcime**
(white).
Mont Saint-Hilaire, Quebec.
8 x 22 cm.

*Of all the rare minerals found at Mont
Saint-Hilaire, serandite is perhaps the
most renowned. Globally, analcime is a
much more common mineral, though few
localities have produced crystals as large
and sharp as those from Mont Saint-
Hilaire.*

purely empirical, their similarity leads me to speculate that such a crystallization sequence may be characteristic of agpaitic pegmatites.

Of all known occurrences of agpaitic pegmatites, no single one has produced as many mineral species (nearly 300 at the time of this writing, 28 of which are new to science) or as many large, well-crystallized specimens as Mont Saint-Hilaire, Quebec, has. No other locality has produced equally splendid rosettes of catapleiite crystals (up to 20 cm) or similarly fabulous crystals of orange serandite [PLATE 34]. Mont Saint-Hilaire is one of the world's most important mineral localities, but why? What unique set of circumstances brought about its mineralogical importance?

Commercial quarrying operations there have removed a large volume of rock, providing collecting opportunities for hundreds of people, and many keenly interested private collectors have brought their finds to the attention of professionals who could identify them properly. Nature has had significant input, too. Three episodes of magmatic intrusion are evident at Mont Saint-Hilaire. Partial assimilation of rock inclusions from earlier intrusions by later intrusions, as well as assimilation of overlying sedimentary rocks diversified the compositions of the magmas. Of key significance, however, is that before it was emplaced, the last intrusion of magma encountered and mixed with a brine, which explains both the enrichment of sodium, manganese, chlorine, and bromine in these rocks and the high volatile content, which was required to produce the explosively fractured rocks that characterize them. Of great importance, too, is that this final magma evolved to a pegmatite stage.

The formation of pegmatites was no doubt facilitated by the addition of volatiles from at least three sources: the original magma, the brine, and the overlying sediments. Finally, the pegmatite stage was able to express itself in more than one way at Mont Saint-Hilaire: as dikes, miarolitic cavities, and in-fillings in fractured rocks, depending on the quantity of fluids involved, the concentration of volatiles, and the confining pressure and mobility of fluids within the enclosing rock. All these factors combined to produce many small, unique pegmatites, each of which differentiated by the "law of constant rejection" to form the myriad exotic, rare minerals for which Mont Saint-Hilaire is famous ●

chapter ten

Summary of Crystallization

in Magmas

WE have examined one important process by which minerals are formed: the crystallization of magma, or molten rock. Most magmas are created when heat from the Earth's interior melts rocks in the upper mantle or crust. As a magma cools, crystallization organizes randomly arranged atoms or groups of atoms in the liquid magma into orderly, symmetric arrangements to form crystals of individual minerals. Those with the highest melting points are the first to form, followed by minerals with successively lower melting points. As different minerals crystallize, they remove specific chemical elements from the melt, changing its composition. The elements removed are those whose atoms are of a size and charge suited to fit the available spaces in the structures of the forming crystals. The continual compositional change in the magma through the selective removal of specific elements by crystallization is known as differentiation. ❡ Atoms of unusual size or charge do not fit into the forming crystals and thus accumulate in the liquid fraction of the melt along with water and other volatile components. The resulting late-stage magmas often produce the most interesting and diverse minerals. The specific minerals that form depend largely on two factors: the initial composition of the magma, and its cooling history. Contamination by assimilation or diffusion, as well as segregation of immiscible components, can alter a magma's chemistry, and too-rapid cooling can halt differentiation. Generally, rocks that host more-interesting and diverse minerals have cooled more slowly, taking more time to differentiate and growing larger crystals. Some of the largest crystals known are found in granitic pegmatites, where their growth probably was promoted by slow cooling, the fluxing action of boron or other elements, and favorable conditions for diffusion due to the presence of volatiles ●

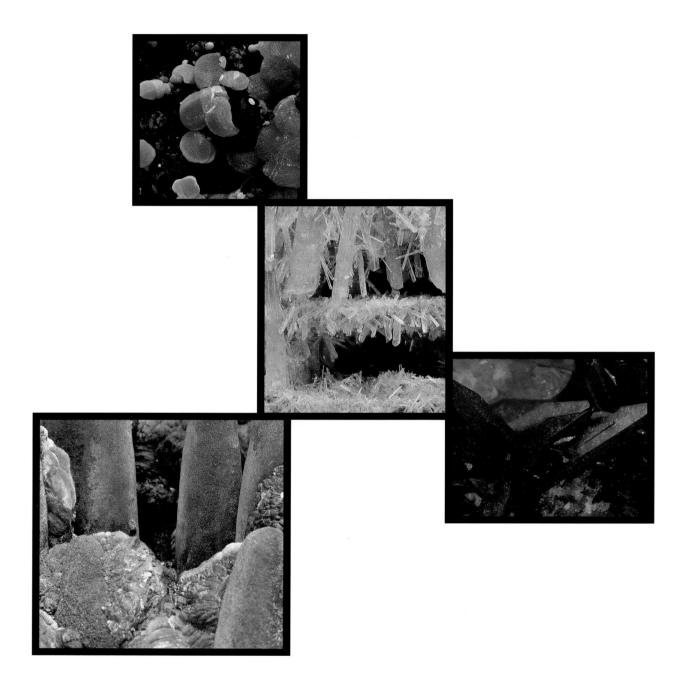

PART III

Minerals and Water

chapter eleven

Dissolution and Precipitation

WATER is perhaps the most important substance on the Earth. It is a unique compound that makes soil out of mountains, drives chemical reactions, and supports life as we know it. Without water, not only would no life exist on the Earth, but probably there would not be as many well-crystallized minerals. As we learned in Part I, minerals are nature's inorganic chemicals, and like chemicals stored in jars in a laboratory, most minerals require water to dissolve them and enable them to react with one another. For example, salt, the mineral halite [PLATE 37], is a compound composed of two elements, sodium and chlorine. In a crystal of halite, the atoms of these two elements exist as **ions.** Ions are atoms that have gained or lost one or more of their electrons and, as a result, have an electric charge. An ion with a positive charge (i.e., an atom that has lost electrons) is known as a **cation.** A negatively charged ion (i.e., an atom that has gained electrons) is called an **anion.** In halite sodium cations are bonded to chloride anions. ❡ Because of their unique shape, water molecules (H_2O) have opposite charges on the ends. Thus, the reason I can dissolve a spoonful of salt in a glass of water is that the water molecules pull the sodium and chloride ions apart. The sodium cations are attracted to the negatively charged oxygen ends of the water molecules, and the chloride anions to the positively charged hydrogen ends. This process of separating the sodium and chloride ions, thereby placing them into solution, is called **dissociation.** Because the solvent is water, the resulting solution may be described as **aqueous.** ❡ The degree to which a substance will dissolve in water — its **solubility** — depends on how strongly its constituent atoms are bonded together. If their own attractive force is greater than that of the

PLATE 37

Halite.
Neuhof, Hessen, Germany.
11 x 14 cm.

As water containing dissolved sodium and chloride ions evaporates, these two elements bond together to form crystals of halite such as these.

water molecules, dissociation does not take place and the substance does not dissolve. Temperature can also be a factor. From experience I know that I can dissolve more salt in warm water than in cold water, but no matter how hot the water, eventually no more salt will dissolve. When that point is reached, the solution is **saturated.** What happens if the water cools or evaporates? In evaporation, the agent that caused dissociation of the sodium and chloride ions and kept them apart, the water itself, leaves the solution. In the absence of water the ions are free to bond together again to form salt crystals, which **precipitate** from the solution.

Regardless of the compound involved, the underlying principle remains the same: at any given temperature there exists a critical level of concentration beyond which no more of that compound's constituent ions can be held in the amount of water available. If this concentration is exceeded, precipitation must occur. Whether the solution is in a glass on my kitchen counter, in a mud puddle in my driveway, or in a fault zone half a kilometer beneath the Earth's surface is irrelevant.

Probably the easiest way to make something precipitate from an aqueous solution is simply to remove the water. This is precisely what happens when **evaporite** minerals form in saline marshes, salt lakes, or seasonal lakes, called **playas.** Such lakes can be found by the hundreds in basins and prairies in semi-arid climates where the rate of evaporation is very high. Their sizes range from a few meters to several kilometers across, and the number of minerals that form in them from a few to several dozen. Utah's Great Salt Lake is a familiar example. Dissolved salts, derived from the chemical weathering of rocks, are carried by rivers and streams to the lakes, which have no outlets. There the salts accumulate until their concentrations exceed their limits of solubility and crystals of various minerals, such as halite, sylvite, gypsum, or borax, begin to precipitate. The least-soluble minerals are the first to precipitate, the most-soluble the last. Bodies of seawater that have been cut off from the ocean may also undergo evaporation, resulting in **marine evaporite** deposits.

In addition to halite, gypsum is one of the most common and economically important evaporite minerals [PLATE 38]. The sparkling pure white sand that forms the dunes at White Sands National Monument, New Mexico, is composed of tiny gypsum crystals that probably formed in Lake Lucero, a playa located a few kilometers to the west, and were carried by wind to their present resting place. Large flowerlike aggregates of gypsum crystals, appropriately called desert roses, also occur there and in other deserts, such as near the border between Tunisia and Algeria in the Sahara, or in parts of the Chihuahuan Desert in northern Mexico. Their interesting shapes make these specimens desirable as decorative curios for tourists, but to a geologist they have a very different significance: because they form by precipitation from an aqueous solution, their existence proves that the area was not as arid in the geological past. Borates, too, are commonly associated with evaporite deposits and include minerals such as borax and colemanite [PLATE 39], which are mined from large deposits in the Death Valley and Mojave Desert regions of southern California.

PLATE 38

Gypsum.
Swan Hill, Victoria, Australia.
9 x 15 cm.

The parallel, horizontal bands of crystals in this specimen probably represent several periods of crystallization due to changing water levels in a shallow, seasonal lake known as a playa. As the water evaporated, concentrations of dissolved calcium and sulfate ions increased until crystals of gypsum precipitated.

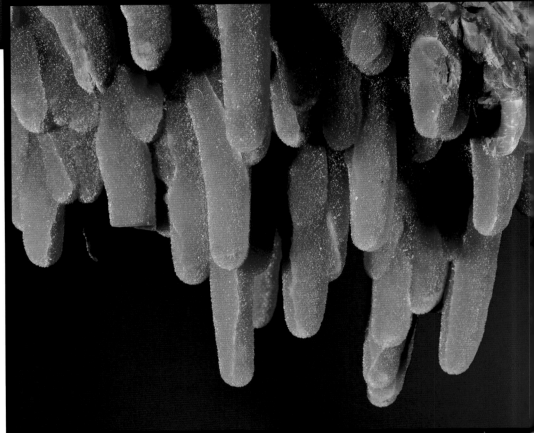

PLATE 39

Colemanite.

Boron, California. 3.5 x 7 cm.

The source of the boron required to make colemanite and other borates in many seasonal lakes (playas) is probably linked to volcanic activity and supplied by nearby hot springs that once flowed into the basins.

PLATE 40

Calcite.

Carter County, Montana. 8 x 10 cm.

The iciclelike form of these calcite stalactites is graphic evidence of formation by precipitation from dripping water.

PLATE 41 *(opposite)*

Opal.

Barcoo River area, Queensland, Australia. 4 x 5 cm.

The play of color in opal results from the diffraction of light by an orderly arrangement of similarly sized spheres of silica.

There are numerous other places where minerals form by dissolution and precipitation. The eerie, cool, dark silence of Carlsbad Caverns, a fairyland of magnificent cave formations, seems about as far removed from the clear, warm, sunlit pools of water at Yellowstone National Park's Mammoth Hot Springs as one can imagine. Yet the same geological process is occurring at each place: the dissolution and precipitation of calcium carbonate. Among the more alluring of geological wonders, limestone caverns are also the product of dissolution by and precipitation from aqueous solutions. As rainwater falls through the air, it dissolves minute amounts of carbon dioxide, producing a weak solution of carbonic acid. Less commonly, acidic water derived from other sources, such as a magma, also may be present. Following fractures and openings in the rock, the acidic water slowly dissolves calcium carbonate (calcite) from limestone, thereby widening its path as it goes. With sufficient time, large openings develop into an intricate system of underground caverns.

In open areas above the water table, contact with air causes some of the water to evaporate. When this happens, the dissolved carbon dioxide is lost from the solution, and calcium carbonate precipitates because it is not soluble in the purer water. When the calcium-charged water drips from an isolated point on the ceiling of the cave, the beautiful iciclelike formations we know as **stalactites** are born [PLATE 40]. Like annual rings of a tree, the concentric bands nearly always visible in cross sections of stalactites attest to their mechanism of growth [see PLATE 139]. At Mammoth Hot Springs the groundwater that forms the pools flows through a large area of limestone before emerging as springs at the Earth's surface. As it trickles over the precipice facing the valley below, the water evaporates, losing its dissolved CO_2 and causing calcium carbonate to precipitate in the form of an elegant terrace resembling a petrified, white waterfall.

Like calcite, quartz (or silica, SiO_2) is nearly insoluble in pure water at normal surface temperatures but becomes more soluble in warmer and more-alkaline solutions. Silica makes up much of the porous, white mineral matter that accumulates around geysers and hot springs and is the major constituent of most petrified wood, but perhaps the most intriguing and valuable form of silica is opal [PLATE 41]. Chemically, opal is $SiO_2 \cdot nH_2O$, where n denotes a variable amount of water that can range up to about 20 percent by weight. The most important deposits of precious opal, such as those in Australia, form when silica is dissolved from SiO_2-rich sediments by groundwater as a result of chemical weathering. The groundwater trickles downward until it reaches an impermeable layer, where it accumulates in cracks and cavities. In dry seasons the supply of water is cut off, and the silica separates as submicroscopic spheres that accrue in a gel-like suspension. As long as the rate of evaporation is fairly constant, all the silica spheres reach about the same size. As they pile up into layers, the spheres form an orderly array, as would equal-sized glass marbles if dropped into a bathtub of water. A small amount of water is usually trapped in the spaces between the spheres, but as evaporation continues, the whole mass eventually solidifies to form opal.

PLATE 42

Barite.
Frizington, Cumbria, England.
7 x 16 cm.

*Barite, together with calcite, aragonite,
and other minerals, is often found in
the iron deposits in western Cumbria,
England, since all these minerals form
by the same process as the iron deposits:
precipitation from aqueous solutions.*

PLATE 43

**Manganese Oxide dendrites on
Limestone.**
Solnhofen, Bavaria, Germany.
12 x 14 cm.

*Like a miniature river delta, groundwater
containing dissolved manganese randomly
spread along a flat, planar surface in
this limestone, leaving behind a trail of
manganese oxide when it dried up.*

PLATE 44

Rhodochrosite.
Hotazel, Cape Province, South
Africa. 2 x 2.5 cm.

The introduction of carbon dioxide to water containing dissolved manganese was probably responsible for the formation of these crystals of rhodochrosite on manganese-oxide ore.

PLATE 45

Wavellite.

Avant, Arkansas. 4 x 6 cm.

Wavellite is a phosphate mineral that can form when water containing dissolved phosphorus encounters aluminum-bearing minerals in a rock.

PLATE 46

Variscite.

Fairfield, Utah. 12 x 15 cm.

The yellowish parts of this specimen of variscite are made of crandallite, wardite, and other phosphate minerals that formed as solutions penetrated cracks in the variscite, liberating some of its phosphorus and replacing it in the process.

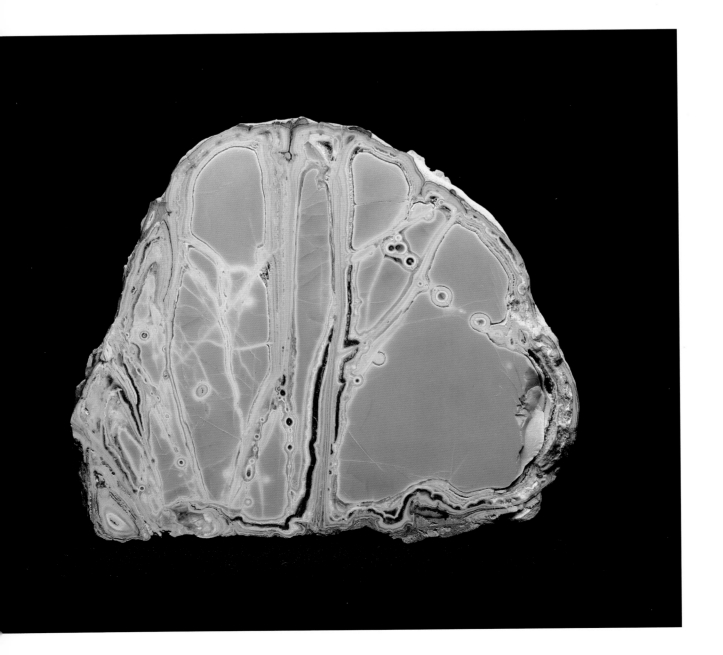

PLATE 47

Strengite (pink) **on Rockbridgeite** (green).
Svappavaara, Norrbotten, Sweden.
3 x 4 cm.

The presence of both ferrous (Fe^{2+}) and ferric (Fe^{3+}) iron in rockbridgeite, but only ferric iron in strengite, indicates that increasingly oxidizing conditions prevailed in the solution from which these minerals precipitated.

In the mineral world examples of dissolution and precipitation of the same compound are relatively uncommon, since most natural aqueous solutions contain other dissolved elements that interfere and cause the formation of additional minerals. One of the most common of these elements is iron, which may combine with other elements to form minerals such as hematite (Fe_2O_3), goethite [α-FeO(OH)], siderite ($FeCO_3$), or pyrite or marcasite (both FeS_2) when it precipitates. Which mineral forms depends largely on how acidic or basic the solution is and on the availability of dissolved oxygen, sulfur, and carbon dioxide, which determines whether oxides, sulfides, or carbonates can form. Stalactitic and **botryoidal** (resembling a bunch of grapes) growths of goethite [see PLATE 9] and hematite commonly fill voids in sedimentary iron deposits and are indicative of precipitation from solution.

Other minerals, such as calcite, aragonite, and barite [plate 42], often occur with the iron minerals in these deposits, as do a variety of manganese oxide minerals (e.g., pyrolusite and manganite), which normally precipitate after the iron minerals because they are more soluble and remain in solution longer. Occasionally the beautiful red manganese carbonate mineral rhodochrosite is encountered [PLATE 44]. Other manganese oxide minerals, such as romanechite or hollandite, commonly precipitate on fracture surfaces in rocks to form fernlike growths known as **dendrites** [PLATE 43]. Groundwater circulating through phosphorus-rich rocks may dissolve some of the phosphate from them and deposit it elsewhere in the form of various phosphate minerals, depending on what other kinds of rocks or minerals the groundwater encounters. Reaction with clays or aluminum-containing rocks brings about the precipitation of aluminum-bearing phosphates, such as wavellite or variscite [PLATES 45 and 46]. Reaction with iron-rich rocks forms iron phosphates, such as rockbridgeite, strengite, or vivianite [PLATES 47 and 67]. The presence or absence of any of these minerals at a given locality depends on whether their constituent ions were present in sufficient quantity to exceed their limits of solubility ●

chapter twelve

Hydrothermal Solutions

IN nature's laboratory, aqueous solutions may vary from a few drops to an ocean in volume, from near freezing to several hundred degrees in temperature, and may be at the Earth's surface or several kilometers beneath it. Similarly, the compositions of these solutions may range from nearly pure water, to water saturated with many dissolved materials. Geologists broadly categorize these solutions as either **hydrothermal** or **meteoric,** based on their temperature and mode of occurrence. Generally, meteoric water is derived from the atmosphere, such as rainwater, and makes up most of the water we see on the Earth's surface or a short distance beneath it, such as the groundwater in a well or sinkhole. Meteoric water is the type responsible for the minerals we have discussed up to now. Hydrothermal water, as its name implies, is much hotter. Its evolution is more complex than that of meteoric water [FIGURE E], and it is usually hidden well beneath the surface of the Earth. ❡ Sometimes meteoric and hydrothermal water are difficult to distinguish because one may mix with or contribute to the other. Certainly the water in some hydrothermal solutions originally was meteoric. Hot springs and geysers are familiar examples. These geological wonders typically occur in areas of recent volcanism, where a source of magma lies relatively close to the Earth's surface. As groundwater seeps downward through channels and cracks in the rock in these areas, it comes closer to the magma and is warmed by it. Even without a near-surface body of magma, as we descend into the Earth's crust beyond the first 1 to 2 kilometers the temperature increases. Therefore, any meteoric water that sinks into the crust or is buried along with sediments accumulating in a geological basin, inevitably will be warmed. The temperature it must reach to be considered hydrothermal water is a matter of opinion.

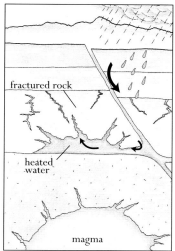

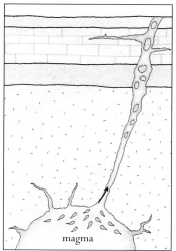

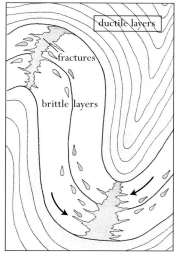

FIGURE E

Sources of Hydrothermal Solutions.

There is no single, universal source for hydrothermal solutions. Some are simply hot meteoric water. Others may evolve from magma or be driven from the rocks by heat and pressure during burial or tectonic events.

Hydrothermal solutions also may be generated by magmatic or tectonic processes [see FIGURE E], and the vein-type deposits they produce historically have supplied a significant percentage of the world's gold, silver, copper, and other metals. The idea that mineral deposits might form by deposition from hot, watery solutions is not new. As early as 1546 the "father of mineralogy," Georgius Agricola, proposed that veins of ore minerals form by rainwater circulating deep into the Earth's crust and depositing dissolved minerals in open channels. A century later the French philosopher René Descartes postulated that these mineralizing solutions originate from molten rock deep in the interior of the Earth. Who was correct? They both were. In Part II we saw how differentiation concentrates certain metals and volatile components, such as water, in the leftover, residual magmatic fluids. These hot, aqueous fluids are one type of hydrothermal solution, and the metal vein-type deposits they form are found in and around large bodies of granitic rocks throughout the world. We also find similar metal-bearing hydrothermal vein deposits in folded mountain belts and other zones of high tectonic activity, such as along plate boundaries, where there are no apparent magmatic or meteoric sources available. In these cases the tectonic activity itself provides the heat and pressure required to "squeeze" out and force the water through the rocks.

Mineralization by precipitation from aqueous solutions, whether hydrothermal or meteoric, follows a common pattern. Water travels through open spaces or permeable sections of the Earth's crust, such as along faults or through porous rocks, dissolving soluble minerals as it goes. If the water is hot, it dissolves even more minerals. As we will see in Part IV, the solution may chemically alter the rocks through which it passes and itself be changed in composition by these reactions. Whenever one of the components dissolved in the solution exceeds its solubility limit, it precipitates. Any number of factors, such as evaporation of the water, falling temperature or pressure, reaction with the wall rock, or mixing with other solutions, can cause the solubility limits of one or more dissolved components to be exceeded.

This process is the general way that minerals crystallize from aqueous solutions. Remember, though, that the specific chemical reactions involved in mineral dissolution, transport, and deposition are governed by complex physical and chemical mechanisms, many of which are still poorly understood. Not the least of these is the process of crystal growth itself. Because they typically grow unimpeded in open spaces, crystals precipitated from aqueous solutions are frequently very well formed and are among the most spectacular examples of the mineral world●

chapter thirteen

Warming the Rain

AT the Earth's surface weathering and erosion are constantly at work, wearing down mountains into soil. Running water, probably the single most important agent of erosion, carries the soil from the mountains to the plains or sea, where it accumulates as sediment. It is not surprising, then, that sediments commonly contain up to 20 percent water trapped in pore spaces. On the continents sediments tend to collect in broad, low areas known as **basins.** The basins themselves often contain marine sediments, indicating their former existence as seafloors that were uplifted by tectonic movements as the continents evolved. As sediments accumulate in basins, they are compacted under their own weight and warmed by the Earth's heat as they are buried deeply under more sediments or occasional lava flows. Such burial may result in temperatures as high as 250 to 300°C, causing organic materials and hydrated minerals like gypsum or clays to give up more water. Of course, additional water may always flow into the basin from above or from along its margins following porous layers. As the water is warmed by burial, its ability to dissolve the minerals it contacts increases. Evaporite minerals, such as halite and gypsum, are common in sediments and are a source of soluble chlorides and sulfates, which form a **brine** when they dissolve. The addition of these ions to the solution greatly increases its capacity to dissolve metals such as copper, lead, and zinc by forming complex ions that are more stable (i.e., less likely to precipitate) at lower temperatures. ◖ Driven by differences in pressure, temperature, and elevation, solutions may travel great distances through basins, following porous sediments or the open spaces of fractured rocks. Carbonate rocks, such as limestones or dolostones (limestones in which calcite is replaced by

PLATE 48

Calcite and Chalcopyrite.
Sweetwater mine, Reynolds County, Missouri. 22-cm crystal.

Resembling a spire on a Gothic cathedral, such large crystals of calcite are relatively common in MVT deposits.

PLATE 49

Galena on Dolomite and Sphalerite.
Joplin, Missouri. 2-cm crystal.

The repeated association of these minerals in MVT deposits around the world suggests that their origins are closely linked.

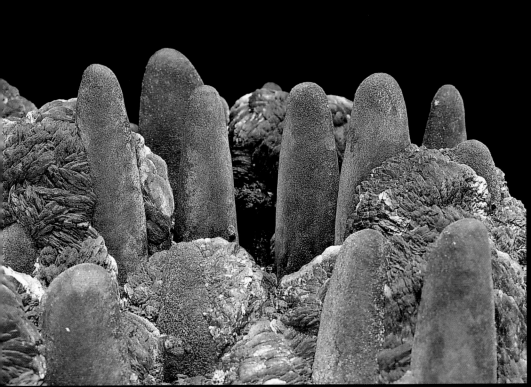

PLATE 50

Marcasite.
Shullsburg, Wisconsin. 15 x 20 cm.

The presence of stalactites of marcasite and other minerals in MVT deposits underscores the importance of precipitation from aqueous solutions in their formation, since stalactites require dripping water to form.

PLATE 51

Fluorite and Sphalerite.
Denton mine, Hardin County, Illinois.
12 x 19 cm.

The occurrence of sphalerite and fluorite together on a limestone matrix is an association typical of specimens from MVT deposits.

dolomite), are especially susceptible to invasion by these solutions because they are highly soluble and are porous. As the solutions enter open spaces, they are cooled by a reduction in pressure. They also may react with the rocks or other solutions that they contact or be cooled by upward transport. Any one of these events can cause dissolved minerals to precipitate as their saturation limits are exceeded. Perhaps the most famous hydrothermal deposits formed in this manner are called **Mississippi Valley Type (MVT)** deposits, named for the region of the central United States where they have been studied in detail. Some of the world's finest examples of galena, sphalerite, calcite, marcasite, and fluorite have come from these deposits [PLATES 48 to 51].

Some of my most memorable mineral collecting was in the Mid Continent mine near Treece, Kansas, which exploited one of many MVT deposits in the tristate district of Missouri, Kansas, and Oklahoma. Stepping into the infamous "iron maiden," as the local mine operators had christened the oversize tin can being used as an elevator, I was lowered 100 meters below the Earth's surface into an entirely different world. As I walked through the underground maze of tunnels, the light from my lamp was reflected by numerous small fracture fillings of galena and sphalerite, the two main ore minerals at the mine, and here and there a natural black asphalt oozed from cracks in the dolostone. Eventually I came to an area where the rock was much more fractured; in fact, all that held it together were well-formed crystals of sphalerite and calcite. Farther along I encountered even larger openings, some extending nearly 15 meters, completely lined top and bottom with golden-yellow calcite crystals up to 30 centimeters long. Elsewhere I found galena crystals as much as 15 centimeters across and a 2-meter wide fracture zone entirely filled with slabs of rock covered with pink dolomite crystals. Perched upon the dolomite were small, brassy-yellow crystals of chalcopyrite and larger individual crystals of sphalerite, galena, and calcite. It was a mineral collector's dream!

A mineral collector's dream, however, can be a geochemist's nightmare! Explaining the origin of MVT deposits is difficult. Since the two predominant sulfide minerals in MVT deposits, galena (PbS) and sphalerite (ZnS), are nearly insoluble in water, how can they travel in solution to their site of deposition? If lead or zinc ions encounter sulfide ions, as they must to form galena or sphalerite, precipitation is nearly instantaneous. These properties of galena and sphalerite imply that crystals as large as those I found at the Mid Continent mine should never have formed, since rapid precipitation nearly always produces very small crystals. How then do such large crystals of galena and sphalerite form in an MVT deposit? This is the question that plagues the geochemist.

There is no single, simple answer. What is needed for these large crystals to form is a mechanism that slowly introduces sulfide ions to the solution at the site of metal precipitation. Analyses show that most subsurface brines contain very low amounts of sulfur, which is nearly always in the form of sulfate (SO_4^{2-}) rather than sulfide (S^{2-}) ions. From experimental studies we know that

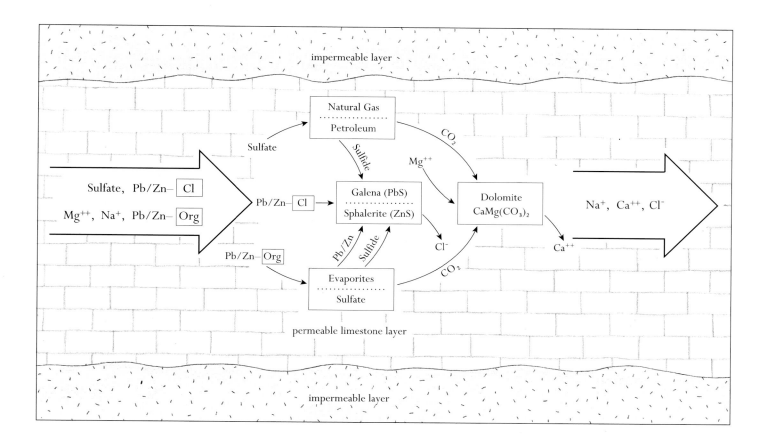

Labels within figure:

impermeable layer

Natural Gas
....
Petroleum

Sulfate

CO_2

Mg^{++}

Sulfide

Sulfate, Pb/Zn– Cl

Mg^{++}, Na^+, Pb/Zn– Org

Pb/Zn– Cl

Galena (PbS)
....
Sphalerite (ZnS)

Dolomite
$CaMg(CO_3)_2$

Na^+, Ca^{++}, Cl^-

Pb/Zn– Org

Pb/Zn

Sulfide

Cl^-

Ca^{++}

Evaporites
....
Sulfate

CO_2

permeable limestone layer

impermeable layer

FIGURE F

Mineralization in MVT Deposits.

Because the lead and zinc sulfides galena and sphalerite are nearly insoluble in water, these metals probably travel in solution as complex ions with chlorides or organic molecules. Reactions between organic molecules and sulfate minerals may provide the sulfide necessary to form the galena and sphalerite, to liberate chlorides, and to cause dolomite to precipitate. Fluid inclusions in minerals from MVT deposits commonly contain chlorides, sulfates, and organic molecules, and dolomite is nearly always present in the rocks.

PLATE 52

Barite on Calcite.
Pennington County, South Dakota.
5-cm crystal.

The occurrence of this barite crystal in a type of geode called a septarium suggests that it was formed by precipitation from groundwater percolating through sediments.

both lead and zinc travel in brine solutions as chlorides and may do so with certain organic compounds as well. We also know that certain organic compounds can convert sulfate to sulfide and that when sulfate is removed from solutions containing dissolved calcium, magnesium, and carbonate ions, dolomite [$CaMg(CO_3)_2$] readily precipitates.

Interestingly, fluid inclusions in minerals from MVT deposits typically contain abundant chlorides as well as organic compounds. Was all the asphalt and pink dolomite I saw in the Mid Continent mine there just by chance, or does each play a definite role in the creation of an MVT deposit? Do lead and zinc travel as chlorides along with dissolved calcium, magnesium, carbonate, and sulfate ions until the solution encounters organic compounds that convert sulfate to sulfide, causing the precipitation of dolomite, sphalerite, and galena? Or is sulfide added to the solution by thermal decomposition of petroleum, bacterial reduction of sulfates, or another mechanism? All are possible, and all have been suggested as probable mechanisms for the development of MVT deposits [FIGURE F].

There are many other examples of hydrothermal mineralization by solutions derived from sediments. In the midwestern United States, such mineralization in beds of limestone has led to the formation of hollow, crystal-lined nodules called **geodes.** The area around Keokuk, Iowa, is particularly well known for the number of fine specimens it has produced. Resembling a cantaloupe on the outside, when broken open the geodes are found to be lined with inwardly projecting crystals of quartz, calcite, barite [PLATE 52], celestine, or other minerals. Similar hollow structures, called **septaria,**

PLATE 53

Mordenite on Cristobalite in Basalt.

Poona, Maharashtra, India.

6 x 10 cm.

Once thought to have originated from basaltic magmas, mordenite and most other zeolite minerals found in basaltic lava flows are now believed to have crystallized from meteoric solutions.

PLATE 54

Stilbite.

Poona, Maharashtra, India. 5 x 7 cm.

Stilbite, here in the form of a bow tie, is one of the most common zeolite minerals in basaltic lava flows.

PLATE 55

Agate.

Rio Grande do Sul, Brazil.

14 x 23 cm.

The variously colored bands in this agate are due to impurities such as iron and manganese oxides.

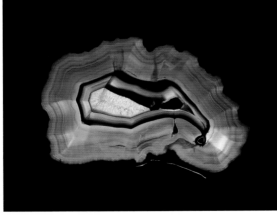

PLATE 56

Amethyst.

Artigas, Uruguay. 6 x 10.5 cm.

The stalactitic form of this amethyst specimen suggests that it formed in a cavity by precipitation from an aqueous solution.

PLATE 57

Native Copper.
Keweenaw Peninsula, Michigan.
10 cm.

Like zeolites and agates, the occurrence of native copper crystals such as these in basaltic lava flows for years led geologists to believe they precipitated from magmatic rather than meteoric solutions.

often contain similar minerals. How and why geodes form is not completely understood. They tend to form around fossils, which probably provide the initial opening for mineral-bearing solutions to enter. As the organic remains in the fossil decompose, microchemical environments with characteristics different from those of the enclosing sediment may be established, causing various minerals to precipitate.

Sometimes things are not as they seem. Because of the widespread occurrence of zeolites, agates, amethyst, and native copper in basaltic lava flows [PLATES 6 and 53 to 57], formed by the crystallization of magma, one might conclude that these minerals also form by magmatic rather than hydrothermal processes, especially any involving meteoric water. But this is not the case. As molten rock spreads across the Earth's surface during a volcanic eruption, two obvious things happen: first, the lava warms the area beneath it, and second, in doing so the molten rock is cooled along its lower contact, like hot fudge poured onto a cold table. If the lava encounters water (rain, snow, a lake, or ocean), it will cool even faster and form a glass, since there is not enough time for crystallization to occur. Rising bubbles of gas often become "frozen" in place, forming layers of cavities as the lava cools, and continued flow can fracture already solidified portions. If a larger body of water is encountered, bulbous **pillow** structures (named for their shape) may develop.

Gas bubbles, pillows, and areas of fractured rock all provide open spaces through which water can flow. As the lava cools, water preferentially reacts

Hydrothermal Mineralization
in Lava Flows.

*Minerals such as zeolites, amethyst, agate,
and native copper that are common in
basaltic lava flows form by precipitation
from aqueous solutions that permeate open
spaces such as fractures or gas bubble
cavities in the basaltic lava.*

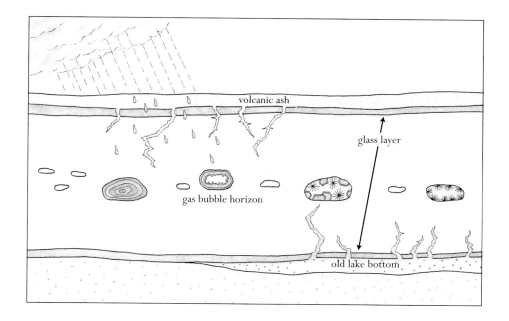

with the glass faster than with the rock (since the atoms in the glass are not
bonded together tightly in crystal structures) and leaches iron, magnesium,
aluminum, silicon, calcium, potassium, and sodium ions from it. Similar reactions occur when water filters through volcanic ash. After the entire body has
cooled sufficiently, various minerals begin to crystallize from the hydrothermal solution that has filled the open spaces [FIGURE G]. Often much of the
iron and magnesium is removed as a thin layer of blue-green clay precipitates.
If the solution is unusually high in dissolved silica, minerals such as amethyst,
jasper, bloodstone, or agate may fill the opening. When the temperature cools
to about 200°C, zeolite minerals will begin to crystallize as their levels of
saturation are exceeded.

Zeolites are a group of about fifty minerals, the more common of which
include analcime, chabazite, heulandite, natrolite, mesolite, mordenite, and
stilbite [see PLATES 6, 53, and 54]. Most zeolites are aluminosilicates of calcium, sodium, or potassium, as are the minerals prehnite, datolite, pectolite,
and apophyllite [PLATE 6], which frequently accompany them. Since water is
an integral part of their structure, zeolites are stable only at relatively low
temperatures. That's why they generally form at temperatures below 200°C.
Many zeolites can exchange cations (atoms that have lost electrons) with surrounding solutions because they have large "holes" in their crystal structures.
This feature has led to their commercial application as molecular sieves in
devices ranging from water softeners to medical dialysis units●

PLATE 58 *(left)*

Fluorapatite on Quartz.
Panasqueira, Portugal. 6 x 8 cm.

Fluorapatite is a common accessory mineral in high-temperature tin-tungsten deposits known as greisens. The hot, aqueous solutions that carry these metals, as well as the fluorine and phosphorus required to form fluorapatite, are derived from granitic magma.

PLATE 59 *(above)*

Cassiterite.
Cornwall, England. 5 x 6 cm.

Because high-temperature minerals such as cassiterite (tin oxide) usually precipitate early from mineralizing solutions, they occur relatively near their place of origin, as exemplified by the granite-hosted tin deposits of Cornwall, England.

chapter fourteen

Beyond Pegmatites

IN Part II we learned that as a magma cools, minerals crystallize from the melt, changing the composition of the remaining liquid by removing specific elements from it, and that near the end of the differentiation period, fluids capable of generating pegmatites with exotic minerals may form. Sometimes, however, pegmatites are not formed, or if they are, the differentiation process may continue beyond the pegmatite stage. The last remaining liquids become enriched in water and volatile components such as fluorine, chlorine, and sulfur, along with metals such as tin, tungsten, gold, silver, uranium, and other elements that could not be incorporated into the structures of the earlier-formed minerals because of their unusual sizes or ionic charges. Such remaining liquids represent one more source of hydro-thermal solutions and are the type most frequently cited as "classic" examples of hydrothermal solutions. ❧ These solutions emanate from the magma and travel away from it, following permeable rocks or openings along faults and fracture systems and forming hydrothermal vein deposits. Accompanying steam may develop sufficient pressure locally to blast its way through to an area of lower pressure, creating a **breccia pipe** (breccia is a rock composed of sharp, angular fragments cemented together). The resulting rapid decrease in pressure causes the solution to cool, which in turn may cause various minerals to precipitate. Breccias also may be created by grinding and fracturing of rocks due to movements along faults in the Earth's crust or by collapse when supporting rock is dissolved away. The open spaces between the blocks of broken rock in breccias provide an ideal environment for solutions to migrate and crystals to form. The chrysocolla specimen in PLATE 79 graphically illustrates this process.

PLATE 60

Tetrahedrite (black) **with Bornite**
(purplish), **Chalcopyrite** (golden),
and Quartz (white).
Herodsfoot mine, Liskeard,
Cornwall, England. 5 x 6 cm.

*Except for quartz, all these minerals
are important ores of copper and are
commonly mined from vein deposits formed
by precipitation from hot, metal-bearing,
aqueous solutions.*

PLATE 61

Nickel-Skutterudite.
Schneeberg, Saxony, Germany.
3 x 4 cm.

*As hot, metal-bearing solutions that
emanate from magmas migrate farther
from their sources, silver and nickel cobalt
arsenide minerals such as this one may
precipitate.*

PLATE 62

Rhodochrosite (pink) **and Fluorite** (green).
Silverton, Colorado. 3 x 4 cm.

Studying the distribution of certain isotopes of oxygen, hydrogen, and other elements reveals that meteoric as well as magmatic solutions may have played a role in the formation of these and other minerals in the mines of the San Juan Mountains, Colorado.

The most obvious proof that solutions forming a hydrothermal mineral deposit evolved from a magma is a direct association of the deposit with igneous rocks. Often such an association is clear, but if the solutions had to travel some distance from their parental magmas, the connection is less apparent. A clue to the heritage of such deposits may be gleaned from the minerals they contain. Because they evolve by differentiation, the minerals in such deposits are those last formed by that process, such as quartz, as well as minerals containing the elements that were the "leftovers" isolated by the "law of constant rejection." As the solutions move farther from their sources and begin to lose heat to their surroundings, minerals are formed as dissolved components reach their respective levels of saturation and precipitate. Solutions derived from granitic magmas frequently precipitate fluorine-bearing species such as fluorite, topaz, and fluorapatite [PLATE 58]; oxides of uranium, tungsten, and tin [PLATE 59]; sulfides of iron, copper, lead, zinc, silver, antimony, arsenic, and other metals [PLATES 60, 61, and 64]; and even some native metals, such as gold, silver, copper, arsenic, and bismuth [see PLATES 63 and 74].

Similar patterns of hydrothermal mineralization occur in widely separated locations. Mines in the counties of Devon and Cornwall in southwestern England have been exploited for tin since the Bronze Age. There the major ore of tin is cassiterite [see PLATE 59], which occurs in veins in granite, along with a wealth of other metallic minerals: major ores of tungsten, such as wolframite and scheelite; copper-bearing sulfide minerals, such as chalcopyrite, chalcocite, bournonite, bornite, and tetrahedrite [see PLATE 60]; the lead and zinc sulfides galena and sphalerite; and dozens of others.

PLATE 64

Stibnite.
Baia Sprie, Transylvania, Romania.
6 x 9 cm.

*Antimony minerals such as stibnite usually
precipitate from hydrothermal solutions
at relatively low temperatures, which helps
explain their occurrence in veins distant
from their parental magmas.*

PLATE 65

Pyrite and Quartz.
Butte, Montana. 2.5 x 4 cm.

*The simple iron sulfide pyrite is perhaps
the most common metallic mineral in
hydrothermal vein deposits, proving that
not all such deposits contain valuable
metals.*

PLATE 63

Gold.
Botes, Transylvania, Romania.
6 x 6 cm.

*Many gold-bearing quartz veins such as
those in Transylvania are believed to
form from hot, aqueous solutions derived
from magmas.*

An equally important and historic mining center is in the Erzgebirge high-lands near the border of Germany and the Czech Republic, where tin, copper, silver, and other economically important metals have been mined since 1168. These deposits also consist of veins in or emanating from granitic rocks. As in England, in the Erzgebirge highlands species such as cassiterite, wolframite, scheelite, apatite, and topaz occur in the earlier-formed tin- and tungsten-rich veins, whereas sphalerite, chalcopyrite, and galena, along with a number of silver-, nickel-, uranium-, cobalt-, and arsenic-bearing minerals [see PLATE 61] are found in later-formed veins, at greater distances from their source.

Similar mineralogical trends are visible in the tungsten mines of Panasqueira, Portugal, among other places. In each of these regions, the granites intruded tectonically active zones along folded mountain chains or plate boundaries. High-temperature minerals like wolframite and cassiterite precipitate from the solution before minerals such as the sulfides, whose elements remain in solution by forming complex ions that are stable at lower temperatures. Acting like a time-released drug, this process is what gives rise to the elemental zoning observed in these deposits.

Other genetically similar deposits are found in volcanic and tectonically active zones throughout the world. Some, such as those in the San Juan Mountains of Colorado or in Transylvania, Romania, have also been significant producers of gold, silver, and other minerals [PLATES 62 to 64]. One such group, known as **porphyry copper** deposits because they occur in or adjacent to quartz-monzonite porphyries or related granitelike rocks, can be found all along the Pacific Rim, from the Canadian Cordillera, through the Rockies, into Arizona and New Mexico, and extending south as far as Peru and Chile [PLATES 8, 62, and 65].

Because of their obvious close association with volcanos and igneous rocks, these deposits have traditionally been considered examples of hydro-thermal solutions derived from magmatic sources. Today, however, we know that this is not always completely true. The fluid inclusions contained in the minerals from some of these deposits and their oxygen and hydrogen isotope compositions point to the same conclusion: meteoric water has played an important role in their genesis. At some localities the data suggest that meteoric and magmatic hydrothermal waters mixed; at others the magma probably only provided the heat required to raise the temperature of meteoric water sufficiently to enable it to leach metals from the surrounding rock and redistribute them in cooler, fractured rocks it encountered as it migrated away from the heat source. The occurrence of a mineral in a vein of an igneous rock does not alone prove that it was formed by an igneous process ●

chapter fifteen

The Effect of Tectonism

WHEN plates collide, tremendous compressional forces cause some to break and others to be folded like an accordion, depending on their composition and degree of brittleness. When the accompanying heat and pressure are great enough, existing minerals recrystallize, producing metamorphic rocks. Among other effects, this same heat and pressure can liberate water from the rocks, which flows into areas of lower pressure such as fractures or other open spaces. As it flows through the rocks, the heated water dissolves some of the minerals it encounters, forming a hydrothermal solution. The minerals that precipitate from such hydrothermal solutions depend on several factors: the initial composition of the fluid released, the composition of the rocks through which they flow, how long they are in contact with these rocks, the pressure and temperature, and the rate at which the pressure and temperature change at the site of crystallization.

❦ Because they are derived from the rocks in which they are found, the minerals in this type of hydrothermal deposit must have a chemical makeup consisting of combinations of the elements in those rocks. (No matter how hard you squeeze a tea bag, it will never give you coffee.) This point is well illustrated by two famous and very different localities, one in central Arkansas, the other just 35 kilometers from the Arctic Ocean, in Canada's Yukon Territory. At the Arkansas location, about 300 million years ago the collision of the African and North American plates caused the birth of the Ouachita Mountains, leading eventually to the creation of the entire Appalachian range. Today, we find hundreds of widespread veins of quartz crystals [PLATE 66] in the Ouachitas, especially in the area between Hot Springs and Mount Ida, Arkansas. Quartz crystals are abundant here because

PLATE 66

Quartz.
Hot Springs, Arkansas. 5 x 9 cm.

Because quartz is the major constituent of the rocks from which they were derived, the hydrothermal solutions that once filled fractures in the rocks near Hot Springs, Arkansas, could produce few other minerals.

PLATE 67

Vivianite.
Big Fish River, Yukon Territory. 4 x 5 cm.

The hydrothermal solution from which these crystals of vivianite precipitated derived iron and phosphorus from the rocks around it.

the rock that was tilted and fractured by the ancient tectonic forces that formed the Ouachitas is relatively pure sandstone, composed almost entirely of one mineral: quartz. The hydrothermal water that was activated as a result of the tectonic activity had little else available to dissolve and precipitate.

Rocks of the Rapid Creek-Big Fish River area in the Yukon Territory host more complex examples of minerals formed from hydrothermal solutions activated by tectonic processes. These rocks consist mainly of iron-rich sandstones, mudstones, and shales that contain an unusually high amount of phosphorus. Deformation and fracturing of these rocks occurred during uplift of the northern Rocky Mountains about sixty million years ago. Hydrothermal solutions activated by the tectonism flowed through the rocks, leaching silica, iron, phosphorus, and other elements from them. When the solutions reached the open fractures, these elements were redeposited as quartz, siderite, and a large suite of unusual phosphate minerals, among them some of the world's finest lazulite and wardite crystals. Calcium-bearing phosphates like collinsite formed in fractures in the calcium-rich mudstone, iron-rich phosphates such as vivianite [PLATE 67] formed in veins in the iron-rich rocks, and complex assemblages formed in veins cutting across several types of rock.

The quartz veins in Arkansas and the phosphate minerals in the Yukon both formed at relatively low temperatures and pressures. When the prevailing temperature and pressure confining the hydrothermal solution are higher, other minerals form instead. If those parameters later change, the changes are reflected in the minerals that follow. Nowhere is this better illustrated than in the famous **alpine cleft** deposits found throughout the Alps in Switzerland, Austria, France, and Italy.

High in the Swiss Alps near the Grimsel and Furka passes, some of the world's finest crystals of quartz and pink fluorite have been collected from clefts in granitic rocks. One of the most famous finds was made over a century ago by a team of **strahlers** near the Tiefen Glacier. Strahlers are highly skilled mountain guides who specialize in finding and collecting minerals from alpine clefts, a Swiss tradition that has prevailed to the present. Suspicious about a quartz vein high above them in the cliff face, the Tiefen Glacier team made their way up the wall, where they excavated the vein for several days. Eventually they encountered a small, dark hole, which when opened up, proved to be one of the largest alpine clefts ever discovered. Measuring 6 x 4 x 2 meters, the cleft was full of soft, dark green chlorite embedded with huge, perfectly formed crystals of quartz weighing more than 100 kilograms and nearly a meter long. For the next eight days almost the entire population of the nearby village of Gutannen pitched in to assist in removing the crystals. Some of these wondrous specimens can be seen today in the Natural History Museum in Bern.

Although they seldom find crystals of such proportions, present-day strahlers continue to collect equally fine but smaller crystals of quartz, pink fluorite, hematite [PLATE 68], and other minerals from similar occurrences throughout the Alps. Clefts containing minerals with more varied compositions, such as anatase, brookite, titanite [PLATE 69], or epidote [PLATE 70], occur in

PLATE 69

Titanite (yellow) **and Orthoclase** (white).
Stubachtal, Salzburg, Austria.
3.5 x 5 cm.

The tiny, green flakes of chlorite adhering to the other minerals on this specimen are characteristic of alpine cleft deposits.

PLATE 70

Epidote.
Untersulzbachtal, Salzburg, Austria.
4 x 4.5 cm.

Overlooking the Grossvenediger Glacier high in the Austrian Alps, this famous alpine cleft deposit has produced what most experts agree are the world's finest crystals of epidote.

PLATE 68

Hematite.
Cavradi, Grisons, Switzerland.
3.5 x 5 cm.

Crystals of hematite such as this one, known as eisenrosen, or "iron roses," are classic examples of alpine cleft minerals. The tiny red crystals aligned on their faces are the mineral rutile.

PLATE 71

Benitoite (blue) **and Neptunite**
(black).
San Benito County, California.
4 x 5 cm.

*The proximity of compositionally different
rocks is probably what provided the
unlikely combination of elements (K, Na,
Li, Fe, Mn, Ba, Ti, Si and O) contained in
these rare minerals.*

PLATE 72

Jordanite (silver) **and Sphalerite**
(amber) **in Marble.**
Lengenbach quarry, Binn, Valais,
Switzerland. 3 x 4 cm.

*As tectonic forces gave birth to the Alps,
they also provided the means to generate
the hydrothermal solutions responsible for
these and many other minerals.*

rocks possessing a greater diversity of elements as source materials for the hydrothermal solutions. At the famous locality for epidote in the Untersulz-bachtal in the Austrian Alps, tectonic activity that metamorphosed layers of sedimentary and volcanic rocks approximately thirty million years ago also produced clefts lined with epidote and other minerals. The presence of calcium, aluminum, iron, and silicon in the nearby rocks and the elevated temperature and pressure provided by the collision of the African and European plates enabled the epidote to form. The occurrence of bent as well as broken and healed epidote crystals suggests that the tectonic forces remained active during crystallization of the cleft minerals. Ironically, the same tectonic forces that provided the conditions necessary to form the clefts also halted their development, for their continued lifting up of the land enabled erosion to wear it away, thus decreasing both temperature and pressure by removal of the overlying rock.

Many other minerals form from hydrothermal solutions generated by tectonic forces, each following a similar pattern. The tectonic setting provides the heat and pressure to liberate the water, and the enclosing rock provides the chemical elements that form the solution. Therefore, the more variable and numerous the rocks, the more unusual and exotic the minerals that form. Sometimes the assemblages are unique. The rare barium titanium silicate mineral benitoite [PLATE 71] occurs with neptunite in natrolite-filled fractures in serpentine only near the headwater of the San Benito River in California. The Lengenbach quarry near Binn, Valais, Switzerland, is home to jordanite [PLATE 72] and some other very rare lead arsenic sulfide minerals, since those were the elements available from the surrounding rocks. Similarly, the beautiful magenta mineral kämmererite [PLATE 73] occurs in fractured chromite at Erzurum, Anatolia, Turkey, because the chromite and surrounding serpentinite provided chromium, magnesium, iron, aluminum, and silicon, its essential ingredients. Even some of the gold in the California mother lode district [see PLATE 3] probably formed when hydrothermal solutions activated by tectonic forces and/or local magmatic intrusions leached it from the surrounding rocks and redeposited it in fractures and openings in quartz veins ●

PLATE 73

Clinochlore, variety kämmererite.
Erzurum, Anatolia, Turkey.
3.5 x 4 cm.

Kämmererite (chromian clinochlore) is found in fractures in the rocks at this locality because the rocks contained its essential ingredients: chromium, magnesium, iron, aluminum, and silicon.

chapter sixteen

Summary of Water's Role
in Mineral Formation

BECAUSE of its unique structure, water causes many ionic compounds, including some minerals, to dissociate into their component ions, creating an aqueous solution. Increasing the temperature may enable more ions to be dissolved, but eventually saturation occurs, preventing further dissolution. When their limit of solubility is exceeded, minerals precipitate out of solution as individual cations and anions bond together to form crystals. The slower the precipitation, the greater the likelihood that large, well-formed crystals will develop. Decreasing temperature or confining pressure, evaporation, and mixing with other solutions are common natural processes that induce precipitation. ❡ As meteoric water flows over and through rocks, it dissolves some of their minerals, causing the rocks to weather and be eroded. The dissolved minerals are carried by rivers and streams to the sea or to an inland basin, where a playa lake may form. Tectonic uplift also may isolate part of an ocean, forming an inland sea. If the rate of evaporation exceeds that of rainfall, the lake or sea dries up and forms an evaporite deposit. The first minerals to precipitate are the least soluble; the most-soluble minerals precipitate last. Important deposits of salt, gypsum, and borax form in this manner. ❡ Erosion transports sediments to topographically low areas known as basins, where they accumulate. When burial is sufficiently deep, heat mobilizes the water within the sediments, creating a hydrothermal solution. Evaporites in the sediment may dissolve to form a brine that enables metals such as lead, zinc, or copper present in the sediments to form complex ions with either chlorides or organic molecules in the brine. Such metal-bearing solutions can be driven considerable distances by changes in temperature or pressure, dissolving even more metals until they cool or encounter anions that cause the metals to precipitate. Lead-zinc MVT deposits, as well as the native copper deposits in the Keweenaw Peninsula of Michigan, probably formed in this way.

Hydrothermal solutions also may evolve as an end product of magmatic differentiation, particularly in granitic magmas. These solutions are typically enriched in volatile components such as fluorine, sulfur, and water and carry metals whose ions are of unusual size or charge, which precluded their incorporation by earlier-formed minerals. Hydrothermal solutions may also be produced by tectonic forces as water is driven from their enclosing rocks into fractures created by the forces. Minerals that form in this type of deposit always contain the same elements that are present in the host rocks because the solutions from which they precipitate are derived from those rocks ●

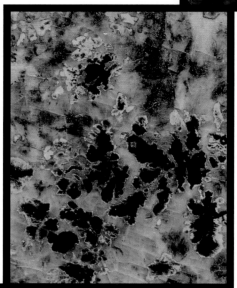

PART IV

Chemical Alteration

chapter seventeen

Equilibrium and Chemical Reactions

MOST of us are already familiar with the effects of chemical alteration. It's the reason we have to take our cars to body shops to repair the damage from rust, and why we periodically have to polish our tarnished silverware. Iron in the steel used to make cars reacts with oxygen in the air to form iron oxide, or rust; silver reacts with sulfur in foods, in water, or in the atmosphere to make silver sulfide, which appears as a dark tarnish. Why do these reactions occur? In the conditions to which they are exposed, neither the iron nor the silver is stable. They "want" to be in a more stable, "comfortable" state for the imposed conditions, a state where there is no tendency to change spontaneously. Chemists know this state as **equilibrium.** ❧ In nature, native iron is comparatively rare at the Earth's surface, but where it does occur it rusts, just as the iron in our automobiles does. Likewise, iron meteorites nearly always have a well-developed outer coating of iron oxide [see PLATE 1], and native silver, which is relatively common in nature, almost always has a dark, tarnished surface of silver sulfide (the mineral acanthite) if it has been exposed to groundwater or to the atmosphere [PLATES 74 and 140]. ❧ Minerals are merely some of nature's solid chemicals, and they react with various chemical elements and compounds in their environment, including each other. The laws governing these reactions are the same as those that govern all other chemical reactions. Water promotes chemical reactions between minerals by aiding in their dissolution and providing a medium in which their constituent ions are free to move about and react. Dissolving salt in water results in a solution containing sodium cations and chloride anions. What happens, though, if the water already has other cations or anions in it? What determines whether a given

PLATE 74

Native Silver and Calcite.
Silver Islet, Lake Superior, Ontario.
2 x 5 cm.

The tarnish on these natural wires of silver formed by reaction with sulfur, just as it does on the silverware in your kitchen drawer.

cation will react with a particular anion to form a new compound?

Chemicals or minerals react because the **products** of their reaction are more stable in the existing environment than are they, the **reactants.** Like a ball rolling down the stairs, a chemical reaction does not stop until the final "step" is reached. The final step in this case is the point at which one of the reactants has been completely consumed or there is a change in the existing conditions that effectively establishes a new environment. Sometimes a reaction that should take place fails to come about. For example, a ball can remain precariously balanced on the top step for a very long time. We know the ball inevitably will roll down the stairs because it is unstable in its present position, but exactly when this will happen is uncertain. All that is needed is a little boost to get things going. To chemists this boost is known as **activation energy.**

In the mineral world, crystals of sulfur [see PLATE 135] may be in contact with oxygen in the air for eons without changing because without activation energy sulfur reacts with oxygen so slowly that nothing seems to be happening. Heat accelerates the process, producing sulfur dioxide by the chemical reaction commonly known as burning. When a ball rolls to the bottom of the stairs, some of its stored **(potential)** energy is converted to mechanical **(kinetic)** energy. In giving up stored energy, the ball (or in our case, the sulfur and oxygen molecules) reaches a lower, more stable energy state for the existing conditions.

A ball will roll down the stairs just as well in your house as in mine. Sulfur burns equally well in a test tube in the laboratory or on the edge of a vent from an active volcano. The chemical alteration of minerals may take place in any geological setting or in any kind of rock—igneous, sedimentary, or metamorphic. The only requirements are a condition of disequilibrium and a source of activation energy. Heat is one of the all-time great activators of chemical reactions, but it is not the only form of energy. Light, too, can initiate chemical changes in certain sensitive minerals such as proustite or vivianite. Even mechanical energy can initiate some chemical reactions; that's why dropping a bottle of nitroglycerin is not recommended!

At equilibrium there is no tendency for spontaneous change. Reactants and products are in a state of balance. It's as if we had ten equally energetic volleyball players, five on either side of the net, each throwing a ball over the net. Players on the left represent reactants; those on the right represent products. Under these conditions the number of balls thrown from left to right by the "reactants" is exactly counterbalanced by those coming in the opposite direction from the "products." The "game" is in equilibrium. How can we make more balls travel to the right? One way is to call out another player or two from the reactants' bench. Or we could let those players rest and achieve the same effect by removing one or two members of the products team from the court. The same is true for chemical reactions in equilibrium.

A chemical reaction may be driven in one direction or the other by increasing or decreasing the concentrations of reactants or products. As we saw in Chapter 11, this is the principle that governs the formation of evaporite minerals. At saturation the precipitating crystals of solid halite are in a state of equilibrium with their dissolved component ions, Na^+ (sodium) and Cl^- (chloride). Adding water, a reactant, causes the reaction to shift toward its products (i.e., dissolved ions), so more halite dissolves. Introducing more dissolved ions, the products, causes the opposite reaction to occur: halite precipitates. The removal of a reactant (water) by evaporation can also reverse the reaction and cause halite to precipitate, as it does in a playa lake ●

PLATE 75

Tincalconite pseudomorph after Borax.
Boron, California. 6 x 9 cm.

This specimen of chalky-white tincalconite was formed by dehydration of transparent, lustrous borax crystals.

PLATE 76

Metatorbernite pseudomorph after Torbernite.
Musonoi mine, Kolwezi, Shaba, Zaire. 2 x 4.5 cm.

Like the tincalconite in PLATE 75, these metatorbernite crystals formed by dehydration of torbernite and have retained the outward crystal form of that mineral.

chapter eighteen

Drying Out

MOST chemical reactions responsible for the creation of minerals involve water. Among the simplest are **hydration-dehydration** reactions. You are probably already familiar with one example from the mineral world, but you may not realize it. Calcium sulfate exists naturally in two common forms: gypsum ($CaSO_4 \cdot 2H_2O$), which contains two water molecules per formula unit, and anhydrite ($CaSO_4$), which has no water. Gypsum is quarried and roasted to drive off its water, then powdered and sold as plaster of Paris. What do we do with it? Add water to make gypsum again! Because the roasting drives off water, it is a **dehydration** reaction. The second reaction, adding water, is **hydration.** ❡ Calcium sulfate is not the only mineral with variable states of hydration. Common in mineral collections are large, well-formed groups of opaque, chalky-white crystals labeled as borax from Boron, California, or other localities. But such labels are wrong. Borax ($Na_2B_4O_7 \cdot 10H_2O$) contains ten molecules of water per formula unit, and its crystals are transparent and glassy. Although the specimens in question may have been borax when they were collected, with time they have dehydrated into the mineral tincalconite ($Na_2B_4O_7 \cdot 5H_2O$), which is more stable in the dry conditions of storage [PLATE 75]. Similarly, the heavily hydrated uranium minerals autunite and torbernite often dehydrate into meta-autunite and metatorbernite [PLATE 76]. ❡ Specimens such as these, that although different from the original mineral, have retained its crystal shape, are called **pseudomorphs** (*pseudo* = false, *morph* = shape). They are direct, tangible evidence of chemical alteration. Because they are composed of one mineral formed *after* the other, pseudomorphs are commonly described as minerals "after" the original mineral—for example, tincalconite after borax or metatorbernite after torbernite ●

chapter nineteen

Neutralization Reactions

L I K E water, acids and bases may influence the solubility of some compounds, and hence their tendency to participate in a chemical reaction. In water hydrogen ions (H^+) are bonded to hydroxyl (OH^-) ions to make HOH, more commonly written as H_2O. In **acids** hydrogen ions are bonded to different anions, such as Cl^- (chloride) in hydrochloric acid (HCl), or SO_4^{2-} (sulfate) in sulfuric acid (H_2SO_4). **Bases** contain OH^- bonded to a cation other than H^+. A familiar example is household lye, which is sodium hydroxide (NaOH). Aqueous solutions of acids therefore contain higher concentrations of H^+ than do aqueous solutions of bases, which contain more OH^-. The concentration of H^+ or OH^- in the solution, which determines how strongly acidic or basic it is, is measured on the **pH scale.**
❦ The pH scale ranges from 0 to 14. The lower the pH value, the more acidic the solution (i.e., the greater the concentration of H^+); the higher the pH value, the more basic the solution (i.e., the greater the concentration of OH^-). At pH = 7, at ordinary room temperature, the concentrations of H^+ and OH^- are equal, and the solution is **neutral,** neither acidic nor basic. Pure water (HOH) is neutral because it has equal concentrations of H^+ and OH^-. ❦ Acids and bases react with many minerals, as well as with each other. The reaction of a base with an acid is called **neutralization.** In water lye dissociates into Na^+ and OH^-, and hydrochloric acid dissociates into H^+ and Cl^-. When a solution of lye is added to a hydrochloric acid solution to neutralize it, the H^+ and OH^- react to make H_2O, leaving the Na^+ and Cl^- dissolved in the resulting solution. ❦ Neutralization reactions occur in nature as well as in the laboratory. As rain droplets coalesce and fall through the atmosphere, for example, small amounts of oxygen, carbon dioxide, sulfur dioxide, and other gases may dissolve in them, producing weak

acids. By the time the rain reaches the Earth's surface it is ready to begin chemically altering some minerals. As the acidic rainwater seeps into the ground, it dissolves salts and organic acids, increasing its acidity. The resulting solution, called **groundwater,** can chemically weather minerals in the rocks that it contacts. As a result, feldspars are decomposed into clays, sulfide minerals into sulfates, and silicate minerals like olivine or pyroxene into serpentine.

We benefit from these reactions in many ways. Not only do they help make soil and provide the mineral nutrients essential for plant growth, but when conditions are favorable, they also produce deposits of bauxite or garnierite, important ores of aluminum and nickel. The large bauxite deposits of Arkansas and Suriname and garnierite deposits of New Caledonia probably formed in this manner. On the down side, as rain falls through polluted air, it dissolves more of some gases (such as sulfur dioxide) than we would like, resulting in **acid rain.** Fortunately, nature has a way of controlling that, too — at least sometimes.

The pH of a solution greatly affects the solubility of some minerals. In areas where the underlying rock, known as **bedrock,** is limestone, lakes appear to be less affected by acid rain than those where the bedrock consists of igneous rocks such as granite. Why? Limestone is made of calcite, which dissolves more readily in acid solutions than in neutral water because of the increased number of H^+ ions available to help dissociate it. The abundant H^+ ions in an acidic lake combine with the HCO_3^- supplied by the dissolved calcite to form H_2CO_3, which breaks down into H_2O and CO_2. In the process the pH level increases to a more desirable, neutral value. The leftover culprits of acidity in acid rain, SO_4^{2-} ions, combine with Ca^{2+} to make calcium sulfate, which is relatively harmless to the lake.

This natural process has taught us that dumping crushed limestone into lakes suffering from the effects of acid rain can help restore their pH to neutral. The same neutralization reaction occurs on the outsides of some buildings, where acid rain has reacted with the $CaCO_3$ in their concrete or mortar, producing a white, powdery, surface coating of calcium sulfate, or gypsum. You seldom have to travel far to find minerals!●

chapter twenty

Oxidation-Reduction Reactions

WHEN iron rusts or sulfur burns, the iron and sulfur combine with oxygen and are therefore said to be **oxidized.** The terminology seems logical, since they combine with oxygen. What really happens, however, is that the oxygen robs the iron and sulfur atoms of some of their electrons. In the broad, chemical sense, **oxidation** is the loss of electrons from an atom. In rusting, atoms of neutral, metallic iron (Fe^0) are oxidized to either ferrous (Fe^{2+}) or ferric (Fe^{3+}) cations by giving up either two or three of their electrons to oxygen atoms. Similarly, when sulfur burns, each neutral sulfur atom shares four of its electrons with two oxygen atoms to make the compound sulfur dioxide (SO_2). Because both iron and sulfur *lose* electrons, they are considered oxidized. But what about the oxygen? It experiences an opposite effect; it *gains* electrons. The gain of electrons is known as **reduction.** ❡ Whenever something is oxidized, something else must be reduced. This is what happens in **oxidation-reduction** reactions ("redox" reactions for short). In the rusting of iron, iron is oxidized and oxygen is reduced. When sulfur burns, sulfur is oxidized and oxygen is reduced. The total number of electrons lost by oxidation equals those gained by reduction, since formation of a stable compound requires that the total positive and negative charges of its constituent atoms are equal. It's like buying and selling: without seller and buyer agreeing on an equitable price, there can be no transaction. ❡ Other, more-complicated redox reactions can occur between iron minerals, as a colleague and I learned while studying the mineralogy of the Sterling iron mine near Antwerp, New York. This old, water-filled hematite mine was one of our favorite collecting spots. Although we never found any of the spectacular specimens of millerite [see PLATE 77] for which the locality is famous, we did collect other interesting minerals that provided clues about the role of redox reactions in their formation. Since these minerals were all iron-rich, the first question to address was the source of the iron that formed the hematite ore. The answer was in the surrounding rock.

The Sterling mine is situated in a body of granitic gneiss (a metamorphic rock with the composition of a granite) that contains local concentrations of the iron-sulfide minerals pyrite and pyrrhotite. Groundwater containing dissolved oxygen readily attacks these minerals, oxidizing them to soluble iron sulfates and liberating sulfuric acid in the process. Immediately adjacent to the pyrite-bearing gneiss is a large body of marble. If such an acidic solution were to encounter marble, the calcite in the marble would neutralize the solution, thereby increasing its pH. A higher pH (i.e., an increase in OH^- concentration) would cause precipitation of iron hydroxide, which is relatively unstable and, with time, dehydrates into hematite or goethite. At the Sterling mine stalactitic and botryoidal hematite appears to be one of the earliest-formed minerals, suggesting that such precipitation from solution did occur. Perfectly formed crystals of hematite coat some of the stalactites or line crystal pockets in the ore, suggesting that they formed after the initial precipitation.

However, there is something strange about these hematite crystals: they are magnetic, but hematite should not be attracted by a magnet. Why are these hematite crystals magnetic? Rather than hematite, these crystals are magnetite pseudomorphs after hematite. In hematite (Fe_2O_3) all the iron is ferric (Fe^{3+}), but in magnetite (Fe_3O_4) one of the iron atoms is ferrous (Fe^{2+}). The only way to change hematite into magnetite is by reduction, which implies that oxidation is occurring somewhere else, but where? The answer this time was among the "interesting" minerals we had collected: stilpnomelane [PLATE 77].

Stilpnomelane may contain both ferrous and ferric iron. The Sterling mine contains two kinds of stilpnomelane — one green, the other golden brown — but both must have formed after the hematite crystals, since stilpnomelane is always found coating the crystals. When we analyzed the two stilpnomelanes, we found that the green variety, which tended to be associated with the magnetite-poor ore, contained significantly less ferric iron than the golden-brown variety, which was associated with the magnetite-rich ore. Thus, the electrons made available from the oxidation of Fe^{2+} to Fe^{3+} in the stilpnomelane probably reduced some of the Fe^{3+} in the hematite to Fe^{2+}, resulting in the formation of magnetite.

With many minerals oxidation proceeds in a much less complicated, more direct manner. When groundwater containing dissolved oxygen percolates downward following fractures in a hydrothermal vein or rock containing native metals or metal-sulfide minerals, those previously formed, or **primary** minerals, often are oxidized. The minerals that form from them are referred to as **secondary,** and the portion of the vein affected by the oxidation is called an **oxide zone.** Oxide zones normally develop in the upper portion of a vein,

The Development of an Oxide Zone.

As groundwater containing dissolved oxygen trickles through fractures in veins bearing metallic-sulfide minerals, many of the metallic minerals are oxidized. Oxide zones usually develop above the water table, where more air is available. In the more-reducing conditions below the water table metal-sulfide minerals may precipitate again, forming a minable zone of enriched ore. (After Mason and Berry, 1968, Elements of Mineralogy, page 141.)

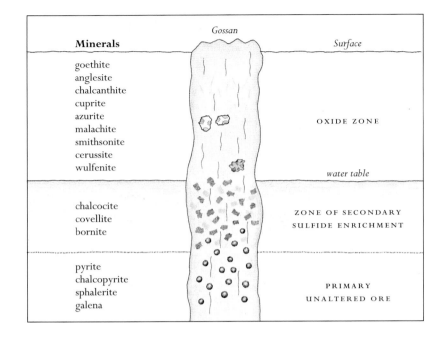

Minerals		
	Gossan	*Surface*
goethite anglesite chalcanthite cuprite azurite malachite smithsonite cerussite wulfenite		OXIDE ZONE
		water table
chalcocite covellite bornite		ZONE OF SECONDARY SULFIDE ENRICHMENT
pyrite chalcopyrite sphalerite galena		PRIMARY UNALTERED ORE

above the water table, where oxidizing conditions tend to prevail because air is usually present [FIGURE H]. Below the water table conditions are more reducing, since the available oxygen is limited to only the small quantity that remains dissolved in the water. Native metals and sulfide minerals are particularly susceptible to oxidation and commonly form oxides or sulfates, some of which may dissolve in the water, causing the metals to be leached away or to migrate below the water table, where under reducing conditions they may precipitate again as different minerals. Zones of **secondary enrichment** formed in this manner may concentrate metals into economically important ore deposits. The rocks in and around the vein from which the soluble minerals have been leached acquire a porous, often rusty appearance, forming a **gossan,** or "iron hat." A gossan often denotes the presence of an ore deposit beneath it. Such structures are often staked by prospectors in search of future mines.

Somewhat analogous are the sediments at the bottom of a lake or sea, where the chief source of oxygen is that dissolved in the water above the sediment. The accumulation and subsequent decay of organic matter depletes the water of available oxygen and forms black, carbon-rich sediments. Therefore, as one goes deeper into the sediment, conditions become increasingly reducing. That's why minerals such as pyrite, that favor reducing conditions, form deeper in the sediment than do minerals such as goethite, hematite, or siderite, that require a more oxidizing environment. The universal presence of pyrite nodules in black, carbonaceous shale [PLATE 78] illustrates the influence of reduction on iron mineralization in such geologic environments●

chapter twenty-one

Lights, Camera, Action!

T HE cast is ready and knows the script, but has the stage been properly set? Just because all the right ingredients are present does not mean they will react. The physical and chemical parameters must not be at or near equilibrium, and reaction must lead to a more stable assemblage. What are some of the physical and chemical factors that determine which minerals form? The compositions of the primary minerals determine the elements available to be released as cations or anions by oxidation. The concentration of dissolved oxygen and the presence or absence of acids (i.e., the pH) may affect the degree of oxidation possible. Dissolved cations or anions already present in the groundwater may cause the precipitation of some minerals if their solubility limits are exceeded. The presence or absence of a particular anion in the solution often determines whether an available cation is transported by the solution because some anions may render the cation insoluble, thus removing it from the cast of players. ◀ Temperature also has an effect on the solubility and hence on the concentrations of cations and anions, as well as on the rates of their reactions. Usually an increase in temperature increases the rate of a chemical reaction. The grain size of the reactant minerals also influences the rate of reaction. Small grains collectively provide more surface area and thus react more quickly than larger grains do. The availability of fractures and the porosity of the rock determine where and how far solutions can penetrate. Locally, the permeability and composition of a rock can be highly variable and can cause the deposition of quite different minerals only centimeters apart. ◀ Finally, there is our old geological friend, time. The longer the reactants are exposed to each other, the longer they can react.

Canada has thousands of metal-sulfide mineral deposits, but almost no oxide zones are associated with them, in spite of abundant fresh air and water. Why? The hard, dense Precambrian rock that hosts most of these deposits is relatively impermeable to oxygen-laden groundwater, the relatively low average temperatures impede oxidation reactions, and erosion by the glaciers from the last great ice age probably scoured away any shallow oxide zones that might have developed.

Many factors may be involved in even the simplest geochemical system. For example, if water containing dissolved oxygen comes in contact with native copper, the most likely minerals to form are copper oxides such as tenorite or cuprite [PLATES 79 to 81]. Whether the outcome is tenorite or cuprite depends largely on how much oxygen is dissolved in the water; cuprite requires less oxygen to form than does tenorite. Because groundwater also frequently contains dissolved carbon dioxide, two other minerals, the carbonates azurite and malachite [PLATES 7 and 82], commonly form. Together these two species probably account for most of the blue and green stains associated with copper-bearing mineral deposits. Which of the two forms usually depends on the concentrations of oxygen, carbon dioxide, and water. Although azurite has a broader range of stability than does malachite among these chemical parameters, it favors drier, less-oxidizing conditions, which are not always readily provided or maintained in oxide zones (because drier areas require more air than water and therefore generally have readily available oxygen). An increase in pH, on the other hand, as may occur when groundwater encounters limestone, can sometimes favor malachite stability. Malachite thus

Cuprite (red) **and Chrysocolla** (blue).
Mashamba West, Shaba, Zaire.
2.5 x 4 cm.

*Similar geochemical trends occur in widely
separated oxide zones throughout the world.
The precipitation of the copper silicate
chrysocolla following copper oxides is demonstrated by both the tenorite in PLATE 79 and
this cuprite.*

PLATE 82

Azurite and Malachite.
Apex mine, St. George, Utah.
8 x 10 cm.

*Hollow molds of former gypsum crystals
coated by blue azurite, partially replaced by
green malachite, record a history of chemical
change.*

PLATE 83

Smithsonite.
Kelly mine, Magdalena, New Mexico.
4 x 7 cm.

*When groundwater with dissolved oxygen
filters through a near-surface ore deposit
containing sphalerite or other zinc-rich
sulfide minerals, it may oxidize some of them,
putting zinc into solution. If the solution also
contains dissolved carbon dioxide, or if it
encounters limestone, the zinc-carbonate
mineral smithsonite may form.*

PLATE 84 *(right)*

Hemimorphite.
Iglesias, Sardinia, Italy. 6 x 8 cm.

*Although pure hemimorphite and smithsonite
[see PLATE 83] are colorless or white, both
minerals occur in a wide range of colors
resulting from trace amounts of elements such
as cobalt or copper.*

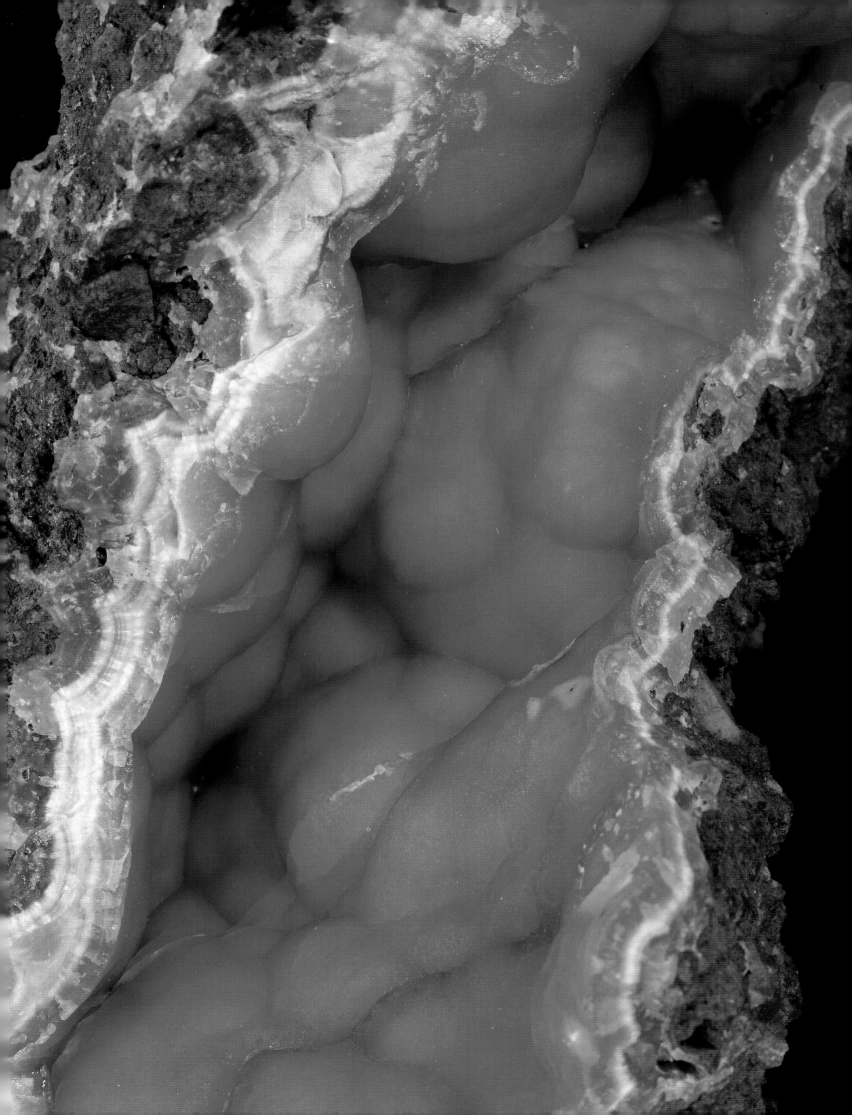

PLATE 85

Anglesite and Galena.
Blanchard claims, Bingham,
New Mexico. 5 x 6 cm.

*Oxidation and replacement have formed
concentric bands of anglesite surrounding
cores of unaltered galena in this specimen.
Under ideal conditions, crystals such as
the one in plate 86 may form.*

PLATE 86

Anglesite.
Touissit, Morocco. 6 x 8 cm.

*When dissolved lead and sulfate ions are
present in neutral to acidic solutions in the
oxygen-rich environment above the water
table, crystals of anglesite such as this
one may form.*

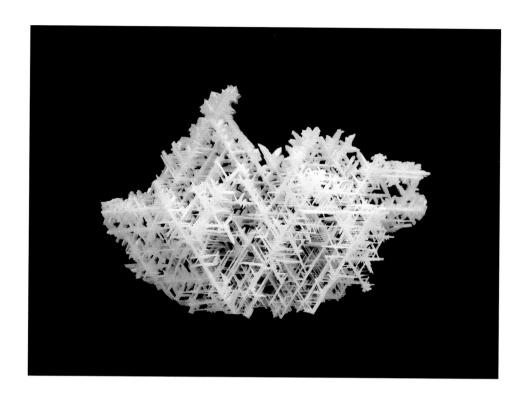

PLATE 87

Cerussite.
Tsumeb, Namibia. 4.5 x 7 cm.

*Resembling delicate snowflakes, these
twinned crystals of cerussite probably
formed when lead, leached from galena,
reacted with groundwater containing
dissolved carbon dioxide.*

is often more abundant than azurite and replaces it as pseudomorphs [see
PLATE 82]. These examples show that the composition of the groundwater
and of the rock it encounters can be just as important in determining what
secondary minerals form in an oxide zone as the composition of the primary
minerals themselves.

Now let's turn the camera to some other actors. So far, we have considered what minerals might form when a single element (e.g., copper) is
exposed to a relatively "pure" groundwater containing only dissolved oxygen
and carbon dioxide. Most hydrothermal vein deposits, however, contain several metal-bearing minerals, and groundwater nearly always contains a considerable variety of dissolved cations and anions. The ubiquitous presence of pyrite,
chalcopyrite, galena, and sphalerite in hydrothermal vein deposits provides
iron, copper, lead, and zinc ions to most oxide zones. More-complex sulfide
minerals, such as tetrahedrite or tennantite, provide antimony and arsenic.

With a greater diversity of cations and anions available to react, a greater
number of secondary minerals are able to form. Among the simpler and more
common of these are the zinc carbonate and zinc silicate minerals smithsonite
and hemimorphite [PLATES 83 and 84] and the lead sulfate and lead carbonate
minerals anglesite and cerussite [PLATES 85 to 87]. Lead is rather immobile
because it forms relatively few compounds that are soluble in water. Unless it
can form complex ions with sulfur or chlorine, which keep it in solution, lead
normally does not travel far. Instead it forms relatively simple secondary minerals close to its point of origin in oxide zones. Gold, too, is a very insoluble
and inert element that must form complex ions in order to travel in solution.
As a result, it forms no know secondary mineral species.

Dozens of other secondary copper, lead and zinc minerals are found in oxide zones, each with limits of stability with respect to oxidation and pH. For example, secondary minerals of zinc—such as the arsenate hydroxides, adamite [Zn$_2$(AsO$_4$)(OH)] and legrandite [Zn$_2$(AsO$_4$)(OH)·H$_2$O] [PLATE 90], and the carbonate hydroxides, aurichalcite [(Zn,Cu)$_5$(CO$_3$)$_2$(OH)$_6$] [PLATE 89] and rosasite [(Cu,Zn)$_2$(CO$_3$)(OH)$_2$]—favor basic conditions and require a highly oxidizing environment for their formation. All these minerals contain OH$^-$ as an essential ingredient, and both their arsenic and their copper exist in states of high oxidation. It is not surprising that all four of these minerals occur both at the Ojeula mine, near Mapimi, Durango, Mexico, and at Tsumeb, Namibia, since at each locality primary zinc, copper and arsenic sulfide minerals (e.g., sphalerite, tennantite or arsenopyrite) were exposed to aerated groundwater which oxidized them, providing the cations and anions essential to form these minerals. Limestone (CaCO$_3$) at each locality probably provided the dissolved carbonate required for the aurichalcite and rosasite, and neutralized any acids, thereby increasing the pH of the solution, and so its (OH)$^-$ concentration. The chemically similar species, olivenite [Cu$^{2+}_2$(AsO$_4$)(OH)] [PLATE 88], is well known from Tsumeb, and has also been reported from Mapimi.

Virtually all metallic minerals are subject to chemical alteration. Given the proper pH range and oxidizing environment, dissolved aluminum, silicate or phosphate ions in the groundwater may react with copper, for example, to form minerals such as chrysocolla, liroconite, or turquoise [PLATES 79, 91, and 92]. Lead may combine with less-common anions to form equally colorful

PLATE 90

Legrandite.
Ojuela mine, Mapimi, Durango,
Mexico. 4 x 6 cm.

*Oxidation of primary sulfide minerals such
as sphalerite and arsenopyrite provided the
essential ingredients to form this rare
secondary zinc arsenate mineral.*

PLATE 91

Liroconite.
Wheal Gorland, Gwennap, Cornwall,
England. 2.5 x 3 cm.

*The world's finest examples of this rare
copper aluminum arsenate mineral are
from Wheal Gorland.*

PLATE 92

Turquoise.
Gabbs, Nevada. 5.5 x 6 cm.

*Nodules of turquoise such as this one form
when acidic, copper-bearing groundwater
reacts with aluminum- and phosphorus-
rich minerals in porous volcanic rocks.*

PLATE 93

Crocoite.
Dundas, Tasmania, Australia.
8 x 8 cm.

*The occurrence of these crystals of crocoite
on a rusty gossan matrix is typical of many
minerals found in oxide zones.*

PLATE 94

Wulfenite.
Mammoth-St. Anthony mine,
Tiger, Arizona. 4 x 6 cm.

*This colorful lead molybdate mineral occurs
in the oxide zones of many of Arizona's old
copper, lead, and silver mines.*

PLATE 95

Pyromorphite.
Cornwall, England. 3.5 x 4.5 cm.

The presence of pyromorphite, a lead phosphate chloride, on a porous, spongy quartz matrix suggests that the small cavities now in the quartz were probably once occupied by lead-bearing sulfide minerals that were leached away by groundwater containing dissolved oxygen, chloride, and phosphate.

PLATE 96

Mimetite.
San Pedro Corralitos, Chihuahua, Mexico. 7 x 10 cm.

The outward structure of this mimetite suggests that it precipitated from an aqueous solution, but its composition indicates that chemical alteration played an equally important role in its formation.

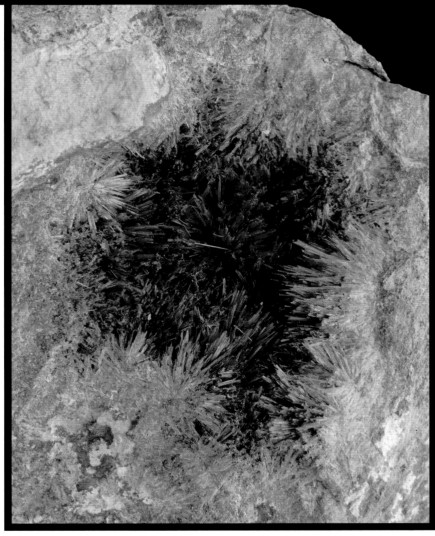

PLATE 97

Vanadinite.
Mibladen, Morocco. 3 x 5 cm.

*Because pyromorphite and mimetite
[see PLATES 95 and 96] have atomic
structures and color ranges similar
to vanadinite, identifying these three
minerals without chemical analysis
can be extremely difficult.*

PLATE 98

Cuprosklodowskite.
Musonoi mine, Kolwezi, Shaba,
Zaire. 6 x 6 cm.

*Under the right conditions the oxidation
of earlier-formed copper- and uranium-
bearing minerals can result in the
formation of this rare copper uranyl
silicate mineral.*

PLATE 99 (left)

Erythrite on Quartz.
Schneeberg, Saxony, Germany.
2-cm crystals.

*Known to miners as "cobalt bloom,"
erythrite forms by the oxidation of cobalt-
and arsenic-bearing minerals such as
cobaltite and skutterudite. The purplish
mineral in the matrix of the nickel-
skutterudite specimen in PLATE 61 is
probably erythrite.*

PLATE 100 (right)

Chalcanthite.
Helvetia, Arizona. 2.5 x 3.5 cm.

*This water soluble sulfate of copper forms
by the oxidation of copper sulfide minerals
such as chalcopyrite [PLATE 8], but
survives only in relatively dry climates.*

minerals, such as wulfenite, crocoite, pyromorphite, mimetite, or vanadinite [PLATES 93 to 97]. Uranium, cobalt, nickel, and antimony, as well as many other metals, also form secondary mineral species [PLATES 98, 99, and 102]. Some of these minerals are locally abundant, but globally they are uncommon because relatively few locations simultaneously have all the elements and the restricted chemical parameters essential for their formation.

Although chemically complex, these minerals are the natural and predict-able consequence of the oxidation of a hydrothermal vein deposit. Theoretical modeling through laboratory simulations of such complex systems is possible but complicated. It is extremely difficult to anticipate and account for all fac-tors in even the simplest natural environments. Even the climate may control the presence or absence of some species, such as chalcanthite [PLATE 100], which is readily soluble in water and therefore preserved only at localities in arid regions, such as Chuquicamata, Chile, or the southwestern United States. All too frequently more variables are operative in natural geochemical systems than are suspected. Perhaps that's why the theoretically impossible frequently seems to occur in nature ●

chapter twenty-two

Which Comes First ?

Studying the order in which secondary minerals form in oxide zones provides important clues to the chemical parameters that prevailed during their formation. This order, or succession, of mineral species, known as the **paragenetic sequence,** is discerned by observing what minerals crystallize on the surfaces of or replace other minerals. Pseudomorphs are perfect examples. The minerals constituting the pseudomorph formed after the original species, whose shape is retained. Goethite after pyrite [PLATE 101], for example, is proof that the iron sulfide pyrite formed first and was subsequently oxidized and replaced by goethite, an iron oxide hydroxide. ⫶ Deciphering the paragenetic sequence usually requires only a good microscope, a notebook, and the patience to make and record careful observations on as many specimens as possible from the occurrence. Since the idea is to look for repeated, characteristic patterns, large numbers of **representative** samples must be examined. Otherwise the true picture may be distorted. For a geologist to determine the paragenetic sequence of a locality based on only a few samples from one small area would be equivalent to a visitor from outer space who, after arriving on this planet in the middle of the Sahara Desert, reports that the Earth is a hot, dry, planet devoid of life. When done carefully, simple paragenetic observations can reveal much about the genesis of a mineral deposit. One of my favorite mineral localities—a small, abandoned antimony mine in Ham Sud Township, Wolfe County, Quebec—illustrates this point well. ⫶ At this locality veins of quartz containing native antimony (Sb) bear cavities containing small crystals of stibnite (Sb_2S_3), some of which appear to be replaced by kermesite (Sb_2S_2O). Crystals of valentinite and

PLATE 101

Goethite pseudomorph after Pyrite.
Windover, Nevada. 3.5 x 7 cm.

The perfect preservation of the distinctive, striated crystal faces on these former pyrite crystals by goethite leaves little doubt concerning their identity.

PLATE 102

Valentinite (white), **Kermesite** (red), **Stibnite** (black), **and Native Antimony** (silver).
Ham Sud Township, Wolfe County, Quebec. 4 x 5 cm.

Deciphering which minerals form before or after others may provide clues to changing chemical conditions during their formation. In this specimen native antimony was first oxidized by sulfur-bearing solutions to make stibnite, an antimony sulfide. As oxidation proceeded, solutions progressively richer in oxygen formed kermesite, an antimony sulfur oxide, followed by valentinite, an antimony oxide.

senarmontite (both Sb_2O_3) grow on the kermesite [PLATE 102], and the whole assemblage is frequently coated by stibiconite [$Sb^{3+}Sb^{5+}_2O_6(OH)$]. Take a minute to examine the formulas for these minerals. Initially only the native element, antimony, was present. Early in the paragenetic sequence sulfur reacted with antimony to make stibnite, but the sulfur was gradually replaced by oxygen as the prominent anion in the system, and kermesite and other oxide minerals formed.

That conditions became progressively more oxidizing is demonstrated by the sequential increase in the number of electrons lost by antimony, from zero in native antimony to three in stibnite, kermesite, valentinite, and senarmontite, and finally to five in the stibiconite. The presence of OH^- in stibiconite further suggests an increase in pH and/or a drop in temperature (minerals formed at high temperatures seldom contain OH^-) occurred. These observations are in accord with the geological setting. The veins themselves are locally sheared and fractured, indicating movement during or after they formed. The fracturing created openings for oxygenated water to enter and form the observed sequence of secondary minerals as erosion of overlying rock exposed the veins●

chapter twenty-three

Chemical Alteration in Igneous

and Metamorphic Rocks

CHEMICAL alteration is not confined to oxide zones and near-surface environments. In granitic pegmatites minerals like tourmaline, beryl, microcline, spodumene, or uraninite that form early in the crystallization sequence frequently may appear corroded or replaced by other minerals. Such minerals are no longer stable in the fluids present near the end of the crystallization of the pegmatite. Tourmaline may be replaced by micas or cookeite, beryl by bertrandite, spodumene by eucryptite, and uraninite by gummite, a bright orange mixture of secondary uranium oxides [PLATE 103]. The dissolution of these minerals replenishes the fluid with lithium, boron, beryllium, aluminum, uranium, and other elements to form even more exotic, rare minerals that are stable at lower temperatures. ❮ Probably the most famous minerals to form in this manner are the secondary phosphate species that arise from the alteration of primary phosphate minerals like amblygonite or triphylite [see PLATE 31]. The secondary phosphates that form depend largely on what cations are available in the fluid, on the temperature, and on whether conditions are oxidizing or reducing. Other physical and chemical constraints may be important for individual species. The available cations are a function of what primary minerals were attacked by the solution. If the environment is not very oxidizing, triphylite may be altered into ferrous iron phosphates such as ludlamite or vivianite, but under oxidizing conditions ferric iron phosphates like heterosite, rockbridgeite, or strengite may form. None of these minerals requires the addition of elements other than those present in the original primary phosphates from which they are derived. In most pegmatites, however, many other cations are available, so

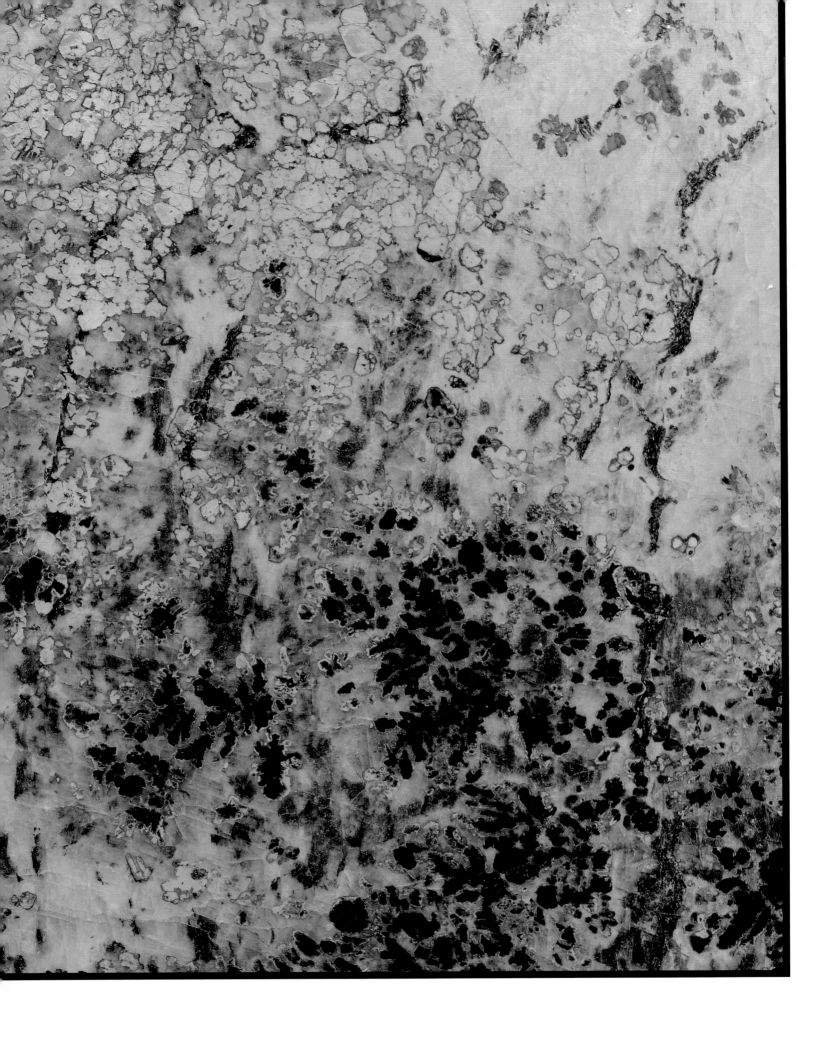

PLATE 104

Eosphorite on Rose Quartz.
Taquaral, Minas Gerais, Brazil.
3.5 x 5 cm.

*Eosphorite is a common secondary
phosphate mineral that forms by the
chemical alteration of earlier-formed
phosphate minerals, such as lithiophilite
and triphylite [see PLATE 31], in some
granitic pegmatites.*

PLATE 105

Hydroxylherderite.
Virgem da Lapa, Minas Gerais, Brazil.
1.5-cm crystal.

*The corroded white feldspar under this
crystal of hydroxylherderite provides
evidence of chemical attack and
dissolution of earlier-formed minerals in
this granitic pegmatite. Hydroxylherderite
is a secondary phosphate mineral formed
by the dissolution of earlier-formed
calcium-, berylium- and phosphorus-
bearing minerals.*

PLATE 103 *(left)*

Gummite (orange) **and Uraninite**
(black).
Ruggles mine, Grafton, New
Hampshire. 6 x 7 cm.

*Gummite forms by the chemical alteration
of uraninite. All of the orange mineral
in this polished slab of pegmatite was once
black, as proven by the remnants of
unaltered uraninite that form the cores
of some of the grains of gummite.*

PLATE 106

Tremolite replacing Diopside.
DeKalb, New York. 2 x 3 cm.

Water and carbon dioxide are probably responsible for the chemical alteration of part of this green, glassy diopside crystal first into tremolite (white), and later the tremolite into talc (gray).

many chemically more-complex minerals can form. For example, adding aluminum to triphylite that is in the process of being altered may result in the formation of childrenite or eosphorite [PLATE 104], whereas beryllium, from the dissolution of beryl, might form a secondary beryllium phosphate such as hydroxylherderite [PLATE 105].

Evidence of chemical alteration is visible in many metamorphic rocks, too. Certain minerals, which formed originally under conditions of much higher temperature and pressure, are subsequently exposed to more-aqueous conditions at lower temperatures and pressures, in which they are not as stable. As expected, they react to form species that are more stable in the new conditions. Because these reactions occur in response to a declining temperature and pressure, the process is sometimes referred to as **retrograde metamorphism.**

One of the best examples of retrograde metamorphism I have encountered is at a small outcrop of metamorphosed sedimentary rocks in a pasture near DeKalb, New York. This locality is famous for its transparent, green, gem-quality crystals of diopside [see PLATE 115], which formed under conditions of high temperature and pressure when calcium-, magnesium-, and silica-rich sediments were metamorphosed, over a billion years ago. The diopside occurs in small crystal pockets filled with a mixture of tremolite, calcite, talc, and quartz. Unfortunately, fresh, gem-quality crystals are uncommon here because most of the crystal pockets have been exposed to solutions that have altered much of the diopside into the mineral tremolite. Many crystals show further breakdown of the tremolite into talc [PLATE 106], quartz, and calcite, probably due to continued reaction with carbonated water. Other common examples of retrograde metamorphic reactions include the alteration of micas into chlorites or vermiculite, cordierite into chlorite or mica, and olivine into serpentine ●

chapter twenty-four

*R*eplacement Deposits

REGARDLESS of their origins or how they are mobilized, solutions containing dissolved minerals nearly always bring about some sort of chemical reaction as they travel through permeable rocks. Frequently the reaction results in the replacement of one or more minerals by others. The specific reactions and how much rock gets replaced depend not only on physical and chemical parameters such as temperature, pressure, pH, and oxidation potential, but also on the compositions of the solution and of the rock being invaded, the permeability of the rock, and how long the solution and rock are in contact. The longer the ions can penetrate the rock by diffusion, the more extensive the replacement will be. Given sufficient time to equilibrate with their surroundings, such solutions can replace enormous volumes of rock, completely changing their composition and appearance. The wall-rock alteration that accompanies the emplacement of a hydrothermal mineral deposit may provide an important exploration guide, since a zone of alteration exposed on the surface may be easier to detect than an ore body buried beneath it.

◀ One of the classic examples of a rock formed by chemical replacement is dolomitic limestone, or dolostone. Dolomite [PLATE 107], the essential mineral constituent of dolostone, is calcium magnesium carbonate [$CaMg(CO_3)_2$]. Although several theories regarding the formation of dolomite have been proposed, none is universally accepted. All explanations agree, however, that it involves the replacement of some calcium in the calcite ($CaCO_3$) of the limestone by magnesium traveling in solution. Seawater is generally considered the primary source of this magnesium. Evidence of dolomite formation is often present in limestone (or dolostone) quarries in

PLATE 108

Quartz.
Middleville, Herkimer County, New
York. 4 x 5 cm.

*It's easy to see how these quartz crystals
got the name "Herkimer diamonds"!*

the form of a "pocket layer," a particular layer of sediment that contains crystal-lined cavities called pockets or **vugs.** Quarries in the Beekmantown, Lockport, and Little Falls dolostones that cover much of central New York and southeastern Ontario and Quebec frequently encounter such layers in their operations. In addition to dolomite, these pockets often contain crystals of quartz [PLATE 108] and minor amounts of the same kinds of minerals found in MVT deposits, since they form in a similar manner. Where magnesium replacement is more extensive, magnesite ($MgCO_3$) forms. Such magnesite deposits have been found in Brumado, Bahia, Brazil, and Eugui, Navarra, Spain.

Carbonate-rich rocks such as limestone, dolostone, or marble are frequently victims of other chemical replacement reactions, involving acidic, metal-bearing solutions. These solutions sometimes cause the formation of ore deposits of lead, zinc, or iron by gradually dissolving the carbonate minerals. The addition of the carbonates to the solution changes its pH and composition, causing the metals to precipitate in situ, thereby replacing the original rock or specific minerals in it. Some important examples of deposits formed in this way include the Magma mine at Superior, Arizona; various mines in the mining districts of Leadville, Colorado, and Santa Eulalia, Chihuahua, Mexico; and the Nanisivik mine on the western end of Baffin Island, Northwest Territories, Canada. The Nanisivik mine is famous for

PLATE 109

Pyrite.
Nanisivik, Northwest Territories.
3.5 x 5 cm.

*At the Nanisivik mine beds of dolostone
were replaced by sphalerite and pyrite,
some of which contains pockets filled with
crystals such as these. The unusual shape
of these crystals was inherited from earlier-
formed, twinned crystals of marcasite,
over which they grew.*

its unusual pyrite crystals [PLATE 109], which occur in ice-filled pockets.
The pockets are filled with ice because the mine itself is situated in permafrost
(permanently frozen ground) that extends to a depth of nearly 500 meters!

The unusual shape of these pyrite crystals is related to the way they
formed. At Nanisivik, metal-bearing, sulfide-rich solutions permeated a bed of
dolostone and replaced it with pyrite, sphalerite, and galena, creating the ore
that is mined there. Originally acidic, the solutions became more basic by reaction with the dolostone. Marcasite and pyrite (both FeS_2) have different crystal
structures. Because marcasite exists in more acidic conditions than those
favored by pyrite, at Nanisivik marcasite preceded pyrite as the stable form of
FeS_2. Flat, star-shaped, twinned crystals of marcasite are common at Nanisivik
and often form a substrate upon which the pyrite crystals grow. The orienta-
tion and shape of the pyrite crystals is therefore inherited from the marcasite
crystals, which act as a template. Most pyrite crystals, which usually do
not overgrow and replace marcasite, more closely resemble those from Butte,
Montana [see PLATE 65], than those from Nanisivik.

Hundreds of other examples of chemical alteration are known in the mineral world. Whether pyrite-replaced beds of limestone or tincalconite-replaced
borax crystals, pseudomorphs provide irrefutable evidence that a change has
taken place. As long as the physical and chemical parameters are favorable and
the products of the reaction are more stable for the given conditions than are

PLATE III

Quartz replacing Riebeckite.
Girqualand West, Namibia. 5 x 8 cm.

The texture of the original fibrous riebeckite has been perfectly preserved by quartz to form this popular gem material, tigereye.

PLATE IIO

Stibiconite pseudomorph after Stibnite.
Catorce, San Luis Potosi, Mexico.
13 x 22 cm.

Probably once shiny and metallic like the stibnite in PLATE 64, these crystals were chemically altered into white, powdery stibiconite by oxygenated groundwater.

the reactants, almost any type of mineral can replace any other. Pseudomorphs may or may not make immediate "chemical sense," however. For example, it seems logical that stibiconite replaces stibnite [PLATE 110], since both minerals are antimony compounds, but why should quartz (SiO_2) replace chemically unrelated minerals such as fluorite (CaF_2) or barite ($BaSO_4$), as it does at Ouray, Colorado, or riebeckite (a Na-Fe-Mg silicate) to form the popular gemstone tigereye [PLATE 111], as it does at Griqualand West, Cape Province, South Africa? The formation of such pseudomorphs often involves a series of reactions induced by compositional changes in the solutions responsible for their creation. The minerals that make up the pseudomorphs must be more stable under the changed conditions, but the number of intermediate reactions required to arrive at these pseudomorphs may never be known. Nor can we be sure that the pseudomorphs we see represent a final, stable equilibrium for the conditions, since our collecting may have intercepted them en route to final equilibrium ●

chapter twenty-five

Summary of the Chemical
Alteration of Minerals

IN reviewing why minerals are subject to chemical alteration, remember that minerals are themselves nothing more than chemicals and that they are stable only under certain sets of conditions. When the conditions change, so do the minerals. The chemical factors that affect these conditions are varied. They include parameters such as pH, the oxidizing or reducing potential of the system, and the presence or absence of specific chemical constituents. Sometimes reactions require activation energy to progress. Another essential requirement is water, which is capable of dissociating ionic compounds into their constituent cations and anions, thus making them more reactive. Physical parameters—most importantly pressure and temperature, as we will see in Part V—also affect overall conditions. Natural geological environments provide a great range of temperatures, pressures, and chemical parameters, which result in a corresponding variety of possible reactions among minerals. ❧ Some reactions, such as hydration or dehydration of a species due to changes in temperature or relative humidity, or the simple oxidation of a metal into its oxide, are relatively simple; others are much more complicated. From the Earth's surface to the water table, conditions are generally oxidizing; below the water table they are more reducing. The oxidation of metallic minerals in hydrothermal veins often results in an oxide zone in the uppermost parts of the deposit. Sulfides are oxidized to sulfates, many of which are water-soluble and therefore can be carried in aqueous solutions through permeable rocks and can react with other elements to make more complex mineral species. When the oxidized metal ions encounter reducing conditions, as they might below the water table, they may precipitate as sulfides again, sometimes in concentrations of economic importance.

Chemical alteration also occurs in magmatic and metamorphic environments, where early-formed minerals are exposed to changing conditions in which they may no longer be stable. Different minerals react in different ways when exposed to changing chemical parameters. The availability of activation energy, the presence of water, the permeability of the rock, the size of the individual grains of minerals in the rock, variations in acidity, oxidizing or reducing nature of the environment, the presence or absence of specific cations or anions, and the amount of time available for reactions to occur all influence chemical reactions. Each mineral has limits of tolerance to these variables, and each will react when those limits are exceeded in an attempt to reach a lower-energy, more stable state of equilibrium with its surroundings. No mineral is immune to chemical alteration given the right physical and chemical conditions ●

PART V

Recrystal-
lization

chapter twenty-six

Heat and Pressure

I T ' S three days after Thanksgiving, and we have a problem: how do we serve the leftover turkey this time? Should we heat it up again and serve it plain, or should we slice it and mix it with other ingredients to make turkey salad or a hot casserole? Whatever we decide, one fact remains the same: the turkey has already been cooked once and will require either reheating or the addition of new ingredients to make a new dish. Like our leftover turkey, previously formed minerals may be changed by reheating and/or combining them with other ingredients to make new minerals. Since the minerals already crystallized once before, they are said to **recrystallize** when heat and pressure involves them in the process a second time. ❑ Where does recrystallization take place? In all probability at this very moment minerals are recrystallizing about seven kilometers below our feet or anywhere else with sufficient heat and pressure to cause individual minerals to react chemically with one another or reorganize the atoms in their structures to make new minerals. Beyond the first one or two kilometers from the surface, the temperature in the Earth's crust increases with depth at an average rate of about 30°C per kilometer. We all know that rocks are heavy. The weight of several kilometers of rock is enormous and is the primary reason that pressure increases with depth. Depending on the density of the rock, a typical increase of pressure with depth in the Earth's crust ranges from 250 to 300 atmospheres per kilometer (1 atmosphere = 1,013 millibars, or 14.7 pounds per square inch at sea level). On the average, then, the minerals in the rocks seven kilometers below us are being subjected to temperatures and pressures of about 200°C and 2,000 atmospheres. Exposing minerals to this much heat and pressure is the equivalent of placing your hand on a hot coil on your kitchen stove and then parking 540 cars on top of it. It's enough heat and pressure to make you want to change the situation; it's also enough heat and pressure to initiate recrystallization in most rocks.

There are, of course, other sources of heat and pressure. When a magma intrudes a rock, for example, much heat is generated, and the pressure may increase locally because of the physical force applied by the magma. On a grand scale we know from plate tectonics that the continents are on the move. The pressure from weight and the stored thermal energy in the Earth's crustal plates is tremendous, and changes in pressure and temperature will be inevitable when these plates come in contact with one another. Furthermore, the changed conditions may persist for tens of millions of years. Because the plates themselves are recycled, so are the rocks in them. Today's marble may have been yesterday's limestone, today's garnet yesterday's beach. The recrystallization of minerals is an ongoing process.

In Parts I, II, and III, I emphasized that minerals are stable only within specific ranges of chemical and physical conditions but concentrated on the chemical conditions. In this section I will show how the two important physical parameters, heat and pressure, influence the recrystallization of minerals. Heat and pressure are two different things. **Heat** is a form of energy; **pressure** is the amount of force acting on a given unit of area. Like changes in chemical parameters, changes in temperature and/or pressure may cause an existing assemblage of minerals to become unstable and to recrystallize into one that is stable under the new conditions. Because heat and pressure are two different variables, they can affect the stability of an assemblage of minerals by acting independently or together●

chapter twenty-seven

Metamorphism

WHEN subjected to heat and pressure, a rock may change both physically and chemically. The directed compression imposed by the collision of the Earth's plates causes crystals of platy minerals like mica or elongate crystals like amphiboles to align in parallel planes, changing the texture of the rock. (You can witness the effect by squeezing randomly stacked cards or pencils between two books.) If high enough, the pressure will crush and smear the mineral grains, increasing their total surface area and releasing trapped fluids. These fluids are critical for recrystallization. Because we usually focus our attention on the minerals, we too easily forget about the fluids. ❡ Without fluids there would be very little recrystallization because the reactions would proceed too slowly, even in terms of geological time. Increased surface area of mineral particles and the presence of fluids facilitate chemical reactions, which may be activated by heat. Some minerals respond to heat and pressure by reorganizing the atoms in their structures into a more stable arrangement; others react chemically with one another to make a new assemblage of minerals. The net result is that the whole character of the rock may be changed. Recrystallization by heat and pressure can induce both textural (physical) and mineralogical (chemical) changes in rocks. ❡ As in all other geological processes, time is also a critical factor. The longer a rock is exposed to heat and pressure, the more pronounced their effects will be. Like crystals growing in a magma or in an aqueous solution, crystals forming by recrystallization grow larger with time. The changes induced by recrystallization, however, must be accomplished in the solid state. The rock may behave like plastic, preserving swirls and folded layers created by imbalances in pressure, but it

PLATE 112

Kyanite pseudomorphs after Andalusite.
Lisens Alp, Tyrol, Austria. 6 x 8 cm.

An increase in pressure or a decrease in temperature was needed to transform these former andalusite crystals into kyanite.

must not melt, for if it does, a magma forms and crystallization proceeds by the igneous process differentiation. It is the solid-state transformation of one rock into another in response to changes in the physical and chemical conditions around it that geologists call **metamorphism** (meaning "change in form"). The process that brings about the change is recrystallization. Both the geographic extent and relative intensity of metamorphism can vary widely. The effects of metamorphism may be seen over very large areas **(regional** metamorphism), or they may be confined to within a few meters or kilometers of an igneous intrusion that brings about only a local increase in heat and pressure **(contact** metamorphism).

It's easy to see how melting sets limits for recrystallization at high temperatures, but what about at low temperatures? Drawing the line between high and low temperatures is not easy. Both metamorphic and sedimentary rocks form under heat and pressure. How then do we determine which temperature-pressure ranges result in sedimentary rocks and which induce metamorphism? The only objective criterion is the presence or absence of specific minerals. We recognize the onset of metamorphism, for example, by the appearance of one or more metamorphic **indicator** minerals.

The presence of indicator minerals and the changed textures in the rock enable a geologist to recognize where recrystallization has taken place. Some minerals, such as chlorite or quartz, may be stable in both sedimentary and metamorphic rocks, so taken alone, their presence tells us little about the temperature or pressure conditions under which the rock formed. Others, such as andalusite, kyanite [see PLATE 5], or sillimanite, are ideal indicators because their presence proves that a recrystallization reaction indicative of a specific range of pressure and temperature has occurred.

Andalusite, kyanite, and sillimanite have the same formula: Al_2SiO_5. The arrangement of the aluminum, silicon, and oxygen atoms within them, which is dependent upon pressure and temperature, is what makes them different. In general, andalusite forms under conditions of lower pressure than the others, kyanite forms at higher pressure, and sillimanite at higher temperature and higher pressure. These minerals demonstrate how temperature and pressure may act independently or together to recrystallize Al_2SiO_5. Andalusite may recrystallize into kyanite by a decrease in temperature or an increase in pressure, or into sillimanite by an increase in either or both of these variables. Similarly, kyanite may recrystallize into sillimanite by a decrease in pressure or an increase in temperature.

The famous andalusite crystals from Lisens Alp, Tyrol, Austria, are proof that such changes occur [PLATE 112]. Although for many years they were thought to be among the best examples of large, sharp andalusite crystals in the world, when X-rayed, many of these specimens exhibit patterns indicative of kyanite! Rather than pure andalusite, these crystals are kyanite pseudomorphs after andalusite, and could have formed only by an increase in pressure or a decrease in temperature after crystallization of the original andalusite.

Andalusite, kyanite, and sillimanite are good examples of indicator minerals because each forms within specific ranges of temperature and pressure. The mutual coexistence of two of these minerals in equilibrium greatly narrows the range, and the rare occurrence of all three in equilibrium defines a unique point at about 600°C and 6 kilobars of pressure. This type of theoretical information provides a powerful tool for solving geological problems, but it is not without its limitations. Experimental conditions only *approximate* natural ones, and the values obtained from them must be used with caution. The presence of trace elements and other chemical components in the natural environment, as well as unanticipated physical complications can change things dramatically!

Nevertheless, if we are mindful of such limitations and account for them, a sound, theoretical understanding of what *should* happen to certain minerals when exposed to specific temperatures and pressures provides us with a means to test geological hypotheses. At present the study of metamorphic rocks is one of the most important branches of the geological sciences because it is crucial to our understanding and assessment of the plate tectonic model of Earth dynamics. If we can predict how specific minerals should recrystallize as they accompany a plate on its way down to the mantle, we can look for the predicted results among the rocks in plates that have made the journey●

chapter twenty-eight

Composition

INDEPENDENT of how much or how long heat and pressure are applied to a rock is one other important and by now obvious factor that determines what minerals will form: the chemical composition of the rock being recrystallized. (After all, we can't make a ham sandwich from leftover turkey!) The fewer the initial ingredients, the fewer the potential products of recrystallization. In the simplest case, of course, only one mineral is present. Pure sandstones or limestones, which are composed almost entirely of the minerals quartz or calcite, respectively, fall into this category. When sandstone and limestone recrystallize into their metamorphic equivalents, quartzite and marble, their textures may change and coarsen, but their constituent minerals remain the same. Recrystallization of chemically more-diverse rocks, such as shale or impure limestone, has a greater variety of potential outcomes. ❑ Shale is composed largely of clay minerals and quartz (SiO_2). Clay minerals have various compositions and contain aluminum, sodium, potassium, calcium, magnesium, iron, and other elements. The quartz and clay minerals in shale are stable over a broad range of pressure up to about 300°C, so until that temperature is reached, few new minerals form. The physical appearance of the shale may change as fluids are driven off and it becomes more compact and brittle, but as the temperature increases, chemical changes produce various metamorphic indicator minerals. One of the first is pyrophyllite, which forms by the reaction of quartz with the clay mineral kaolinite. At around 400°C pyrophyllite breaks down into Al_2SiO_5 (in the form of either andalusite or kyanite, depending on the pressure), quartz, and water. ❑ By this time the shale has probably become much harder and more compact and acquired a

PLATE 113

Almandine in Mica Schist.
Wrangell, Alaska. 2.5-cm crystals.

When aluminum-rich sediments are subjected to moderately high temperature and pressure, crystals of almandine garnet may form as the sediments are transformed into metamorphic rocks.

PLATE 114

Cordierite.
India. 13 x 14 cm.

Known as iolite or water sapphire, this attractive blue gem mineral forms when aluminum- and magnesium-rich rocks are subjected to high temperature and pressure.

shiny luster, the result of alignment of the platy clay minerals. It has become the metamorphic rock, slate. With increasing temperature and pressure, the slate will become even shinier, and its layers will probably deform as it recrystallizes into yet another rock, phyllite. Between 400 and 500°C chlorites and micas begin to appear, and the rock is transformed from phyllite into schist. Crystals of almandine garnet [PLATE 113] also may form at this time, especially with an increase in pressure. From 500 to 700°C additional minerals, such as staurolite, cordierite, or sillimanite [PLATES 5 and 114] may form, along with clots or distinct bands of feldspars and quartz, changing the rock from a schist into a gneiss.

In the late 1800s a Scottish geologist, George Barrow, found this precise sequence of minerals in northern Scotland, where shales have been metamorphosed by high heat and pressure. Starting where the effects of metamorphism were the least and progressing to where they were the most intense, Barrow found that the rocks changed from shale to slate, to phyllite, chlorite schist, mica schist, and finally gneiss. He also observed that the minerals in these rocks appeared in the following order: chlorite, biotite mica, almandine garnet, staurolite, kyanite, sillimanite. A very similar sequence exists between eastern Vermont and the White Mountains of New Hampshire, and many others have been documented elsewhere.

The composition of an impure limestone is quite different from that of shale and consists predominantly of calcite with variable amounts of dolomite, quartz, clays, and other minerals. Since these minerals provide calcium, magnesium, silicon, and aluminum as "ingredients," these same elements must constitute the new minerals formed by recrystallization. Exposing an impure limestone to increasing temperature and pressure usually results in the silicate minerals talc, tremolite, diopside, and forsterite. Because the carbonate content of limestone normally exceeds its silicate content, "excess" calcite left over from the reactions that form these minerals is common, which explains why they are often enclosed in coarsely recrystallized calcite [see PLATES 123 and 128].

Because the carbonates calcite and dolomite release carbon dioxide when they break down, the concentration of CO_2, as well as that of H_2O, becomes important in regulating the possible reactions. At very high temperatures, calcite and quartz may react to form the calcium silicate wollastonite and CO_2. However, since CO_2 is a product of the reaction, it must be removed for the reaction to proceed. (Remember the volleyball players from Chapter 17; the game could be won by adding players to the reactants team or removing them from the products team.) An environment of low pressure (likely provided by contact metamorphism), into which the CO_2 can escape, or the presence of water to dilute the CO_2 concentration accomplishes this task.

When limestones rich in silica and magnesium recrystallize, rocks such as tremolite-diopside schists (often with interbedded quartzite) may result. Such rocks are found at a number of localities in St. Lawrence County, New York, where well-formed crystals of diopside and tremolite [PLATES 106 and 115]

occur in small pockets or seams. The famous diopside locality dear DeKalb and uvite locality near Richville (Gouverneur township) are classic examples. By contrast, if little silica is available, the presence of aluminum may lead to the formation of the oxide minerals spinel or corundum, since it is the silicate minerals that normally incorporate the aluminum. The ruby deposits of Mogok, Burma, which have yielded fabulous gem-quality ruby corundum and spinel crystals for centuries, are probably the most famous example. The presence of evaporite minerals in carbonate-rich sediments may lead to the formation of another important gem, lapis lazuli, which is composed of the ultramarine blue mineral lazurite [PLATE 116].

Any rock—igneous, sedimentary, or metamorphic—can be recrystallized. The minerals that form depend on the composition of that rock, the amount of heat and pressure to which it is subjected, the availability of fluids to promote recrystallization, and the allowance of sufficient time for the process to occur. The diversity of minerals that can result is enormous. Rocks such as peridotite, that are rich in magnesium silicate minerals, may recrystallize to form deposits of talc, serpentine, or chrysotile asbestos. Given the right conditions, the recrystallization of aluminum-rich rocks yields rubies or sapphires [PLATE 117]. Seafloor sediments containing local concentrations of manganese may recrystallize into rhodonite [PLATE 118]. At Franklin, New Jersey, metamorphism of manganese- and zinc-rich sediments in contact with limestone has produced a unique zinc ore deposit consisting of coarsely crystallized franklinite, willemite, and zincite [PLATE 119], along with numerous more-exotic species. Hundreds of other examples of regional metamorphic minerals could be cited, from actinolite to zussmanite, but the basis of their formation is the same: each is more stable in the imposed conditions of temperature and pressure than were the initial minerals from which it formed●

chapter twenty-nine

Complex Recrystallization

So FAR, I have talked only about minerals that form during the large-scale, regional recrystallization of rocks, driven by heat and pressure supplied by burial or tectonic forces. All the essential ingredients of recrystallization have been contained in the rocks themselves. Essentially, I have been only reheating the turkey. Now it's time to make a casserole by adding ingredients from outside sources. This is exactly what happens during **contact metamorphism** within a few meters of a small igneous intrusion or a few kilometers of a larger one [FIGURE I]. ❦ The magma provides not only heat but also new ingredients to the rock that it intrudes by the injection and diffusion of fluids. While the heat induces recrystallization, the fluids bearing chemical components may react with one or more of the minerals in the rock, chemically replacing them. Both processes are commonly grouped together under the umbrella of contact metamorphism because both are confined to an area in contact with the intrusion. This contact zone of recrystallized and chemically replaced rock physically manifests itself as a band or **aureole** around the intrusion. Because any type of magma can intrude any type of rock, the possibilities for many different and exotic mineral species to form are great. Let's look at a few recipes for mineral casseroles. ❦ As we learned in Part II, the magmatic fluids that form granitic pegmatites become enriched in volatiles and light elements such as lithium, boron, and beryllium by the "law of constant rejection." When such a magmatic fluid intrudes a rock, these elements tend to diffuse into the rock because their small atomic size and mass usually permits their access to even the smallest permeable spaces. These elements form highly reactive ions that chemically alter the rock and form

PLATE 120

Beryl, variety emerald.
Malisheva mine, Yekaterinburg,
Sverdlovsk Oblast, Russia.
3-cm crystal.

Emeralds in mica-schist deposits have a
complex genesis, involving both magmatic
and metamorphic processes.

FIGURE I

Contact Metamorphism.

Contact Metamorphism.

When a magma intrudes a rock, chemical components are often exchanged, and the local increase in heat and pressure recrystallizes the rock in contact with the magma. A common example is the intrusion of a dolomitic limestone by a silicate magma to form a rock known as skarn. Silicon and aluminum from the magma react with calcium and magnesium in the limestone to make minerals such as diopside and grossular in a halo, or aureole, around the magma.

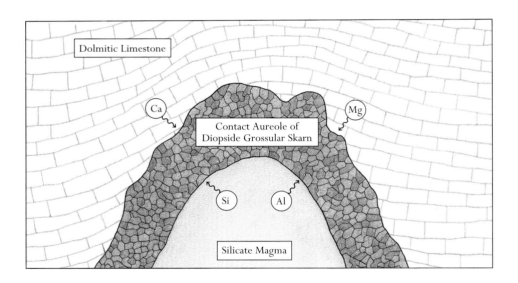

Dolmitic Limestone

Ca

Mg

Contact Aureole of
Diopside Grossular Skarn

Si   Al

Silicate Magma

new minerals. Lithium-bearing amphiboles such as holmquistite, and the magnesium tourmaline, dravite, which are often found in rocks adjacent to intrusions of granitic pegmatites, are two examples. The lithium or boron required to make these minerals is supplied by the invading magmatic fluid; most of the other elements are provided by minerals already present in the rock.

When a beryllium-bearing fluid from a granitic magma invades a silica-poor rock such as amphibolite or serpentinite, a mica schist-type beryl deposit may result. The significance of such deposits is that the rocks that are intruded often contain minor concentrations of chromium or vanadium, two elements that may be incorporated by the beryl to produce emeralds [PLATE 120]. The legendary emerald mines of Cleopatra, near the Red Sea in Egypt, are of this type and are among the oldest mines known, having produced emeralds for Cleopatra, and possibly even King Tutankhamen, over 3,300 years ago. Similar deposits in Russia, Brazil, and other countries are the major producers today. In some of these deposits the rare variety of chrysoberyl, alexandrite, is also mined. Named for Russian emperor Alexander II, this unique gemstone appears green in daylight but red in artificial incandescent light●

chapter thirty

Skarns: Trash or Treasure?

IN Part IV we learned that at low temperatures limestone is susceptible to chemical replacement by metal-bearing solutions. At higher temperatures, near intruding magma, limestone typically recrystallizes into coarse-grained marble, while iron, aluminum, silicon, sodium, potassium, and water supplied by the magma react with the limestone to make silicate minerals containing those elements. The resulting recrystallized rock, called **skarn** [see FIGURE 1], may host a wide variety of mineral species. The word skarn is derived from the Swedish for "waste" or "trash." It originally referred to the silicate-rich band of waste rock (i.e., the contact metamorphic aureole) surrounding more-valuable ore. ❰ One person's trash is another's treasure. Some skarns may contain economically recoverable ore minerals such as magnetite, cassiterite, scheelite, sphalerite, or chalcopyrite, or provide local concentrations of manganese, phosphorus, uranium, and other metals. Many skarns contain large, well-formed crystals enclosed in recrystallized calcite, or marble. The crystals of ilmenite from Arendal, Norway, or Bancroft, Ontario, on the other hand, may not occur in sufficient quantities to be valued for their titanium content, but they are valued by scientists and collectors as some of the largest well-formed crystals of ilmenite known. Likewise, the spinel crystals from Amity, New York, may be too dark and opaque for use as gemstones, but they are among the finest large crystals of spinel in the world. ❰ The minerals that form in a skarn depend on temperature and pressure, as well as on the compositions of both the magmatic fluid and the original limestone with which it reacts. The heat transferred to the limestone from the magma may increase the temperature in the contact zone to nearly that of

PLATE 121

Uvite.
Powers farm, Pierrepont, New York.
7 x 12 cm.

*The origin of the skarnlike assemblage of
minerals at this famous locality is not well
understood because much of its geology is
concealed by overlying sand that was
deposited by glaciers approximately ten
thousand years ago.*

PLATE 122

Uvarovite.
Outokumpu, Finland. 2-cm crystals.

*Most garnet is red, but when rocks
containing small amounts of chromium are
recrystallized under heat and pressure, the
rare green garnet, uvarovite, may form.*

PLATE 123

Diopside (green) **and Phlogopite**
(brown) **in Calcite.**
Bird's Creek, Ontario. 5 x 9 cm.

*These calcium- and magnesium-rich
silicate minerals are typical of skarns that
form in dolomitic limestones.*

PLATE 124

Fluor Silicic Edenite.
Wilberforce, Ontario. 4 x 4 cm.

*The fluorine in this complex species of
amphibole is a reminder of the importance
of volatile components such as fluorine
and water in promoting recrystallization
reactions.*

the magma itself. Therefore, it is not unusual to find feldspars, garnets, pyroxenes, or olivines in a contact aureole, since these minerals also are stable in high-temperature magmatic environments. The concentrations of water, carbon dioxide, fluorine, and other volatile components have a great influence on the total pressure and regulation of possible reactions between the various minerals present. The fewer the chemical constituents available, the fewer and simpler the minerals that can form. The simplest of these are anhydrous minerals, such as magnetite or wollastonite, that contain only one or two metal cations. Vesuvianite and uvite tourmaline [PLATE 121] are examples of chemically more-complex species found in skarns.

Given the elements most often involved in the formation of a skarn, and recalling some of the minerals formed by magmatic processes, it is not too difficult to predict which minerals might be found in skarns. For example, garnets form at relatively high temperatures and include species rich in calcium, aluminum, and iron, elements common in skarns. The calcium-rich garnets grossular, andradite, and uvarovite [PLATE 122] thus all occur in skarns. Like garnets, the pyroxenes, amphiboles, and micas most often encountered in skarns are rich in calcium, iron, and magnesium. Examples include the pyroxenes hedenbergite and diopside [PLATE 123]; the amphiboles tremolite, actinolite, and edenite [PLATE 124]; and the micas biotite and phlogopite [see PLATE 123]. Composed of similar elements, the minerals epidote and vesuvianite also are common in some skarns.

Potassium and plagioclase feldspars both occur in skarns, as does scapolite, because the combination of an impure limestone and a magmatic fluid rich in silica provides all the ingredients necessary to make these minerals. The calcium-dominant scapolite, meionite [PLATE 125], is especially prevalent in skarns because of the universal abundance of calcium in limestones. Large, well-formed crystals of scapolite have been found in hundreds of localities. One very different and interesting occurrence, however, stands out from all the rest: Mars. Some geologists believe that scapolite is present on Mars because infrared spectra from certain areas of the planet's surface closely resemble those of scapolite. Assuming that scapolite does exist on Mars, the requirements for its formation on the Earth, particularly the fluid phase necessary to promote crystallization, suggest that at one time in the geological past Mars had a very different atmosphere and perhaps even lakes or oceans, the remains of which may now be stored in its polar ice caps.

Because they result from recrystallization, chemical alteration, and replacement occurring simultaneously, skarns are among the most complex deposits known. In some of the billion-year-old metamorphosed sediments of northern New York State and southeastern Ontario and Quebec are a number of classic mineral localities that contain typical skarn minerals. Specimens of uvite, titanite, zircon, uraninite, fluorapatite, and other species from these occurrences can be viewed in nearly every major natural history museum in the world [PLATES 121 and 123 to 128]. Marble is usually present at or nearby most of these localities, but in some cases the skarns form curious, calcite-cored veins that cut

PLATE 125

Meionite.
Leslie Lake, Pontiac County, Quebec. 2.5 x 4 cm crystal.

This calcium-rich scapolite may have formed by the reaction of plagioclase feldspar with calcite under heat and pressure.

PLATE 126

Zircon.
Silver Queen mine, near Perth,
Ontario. 4-cm crystal.

*In skarns, the occasional occurrence of
minerals such as zircon, that are typical of
magmatic deposits, is a reminder of their
complex origin.*

PLATE 127

Uraninite.
Cardiff mine, Wilberforce, Ontario.
2-cm crystal.

*Some of the largest well-formed crystals of
uraninite in North America come from
metamorphic calcite-fluorite veins in the
billion-year-old rocks of the Wilberforce
area in southeastern Ontario.*

PLATE 128

Fluorapatite in Calcite.
Yates mine, Otter Lake, Quebec.
2 x 6 cm crystal.

*Did the phosphorus required to form this
fluorapatite crystal come from nearby
sediments or from the igneous rocks with
which its calcite matrix was in contact?*

across or are included within the adjacent metamorphosed sediments rather than the marble. Although the veins often contain large, well-formed crystals, most of the minerals are the same species that occur in the adjacent rocks.

Various theories on the origin of these veins have been proposed, but none is universally accepted. The veins are similar to skarns in that they occur locally in metamorphic rocks, usually near marble, and they contain skarnlike mineral assemblages developed in contact zones between silicate-rich and coarsely recrystallized carbonate-rich rocks. Often, however, no source of igneous-derived fluids is apparent. One interpretation, of course, is that an igneous source does not exist. Perhaps the fluids are derived tectonically, and these deposits are but one more example of how more than one geological process can create conditions conducive to the formation of the same suite of minerals.

Sometimes the mountain may come to Mohammed. We have seen how skarn minerals form when a magma intrudes a carbonate rock such as limestone. On a smaller scale, however, a somewhat reverse process can happen. Because they are of sedimentary origin, limestones can't really "intrude" magmas, but pieces of limestone may be incorporated into a magma as inclusions. The net result is often very much the same: a similar geological environment of high temperature and relatively low pressure results in new minerals being formed as the limestone is recrystallized and chemically altered by fluids from the magma. The resulting minerals are those typical of skarn deposits. Two examples of such occurrences are the blocks of recrystallized limestone ejected by Mount Vesuvius, Italy, and the marble inclusions that occur in the nepheline syenite at Mont Saint-Hilaire, Quebec. Probably the most famous mineral formed in such a manner is the namesake of Mount Vesuvius, vesuvianite [see PLATE 130], which occurs along with other common skarn minerals at both localities●

chapter thirty-one

Rodingites

LIKE skarns, rodingites have a complex origin. In Chapter 15 I explained how some hydrothermal solutions evolve from tectonic processes to produce alpine cleft and related vein-type deposits. The essential elements of the minerals in the clefts and veins were provided by the enclosing rock, the gross character and composition of which remained relatively unchanged. As these same solutions travel farther from their points of origin and encounter rocks of different compositions, however, they may chemically alter the enclosing rocks, producing new suites of minerals. **Rodingites** are one example of rocks formed in this way. ❦ Although their origin is not completely understood, it is generally agreed that rodingites represent chemically altered granitic dikes that are associated with metamorphosed oceanic crustal rocks scraped off a tectonic plate during continental collisions [FIGURE J]. Rodingites occur in folded mountain chains throughout the world. The elevated temperature and pressure provided by the converging plates liberate hydrothermal solutions that chemically alter the olivine and pyroxene in the magnesium-rich oceanic crustal rocks into serpentinite and convert some of the granitic dikes into rodingites. The more-famous and better-studied rodingites of North America are in the northern Appalachians, which extend from northern Vermont, through southeastern Quebec, to Newfoundland. Similar occurrences can be found in the Ural Mountains of Russia, Pakistan, and numerous localities in northern Italy and southern Tyrol, Austria. ❦ Some of the world's finest examples of grossular, diopside, vesuvianite, clinochlore, and other minerals have come from these deposits [PLATES 129 to 131]. Many of these minerals from widely separated localities such as

Asbestos, Quebec; Eden Mills, Vermont; and Asbest, Russia, are indistinguishable from each other, suggesting that similar geological conditions once existed at each of these places. Grossular from each of these localities ranges in color from pale pink to bright orange; some specimens are even emerald green. Green grossular owes its color to chromium, originally present in the magnesium-rich rocks as chromite and made available to the grossular by the fluids moving through and chemically altering the rocks. The cores of many of the green grossular crystals from Asbestos, Quebec, contain a tiny grain of chromite. Andradite garnet also occurs in some rodingites. The most famous locality is probably Val Malenco, Lombardy, Italy, where the green, gem variety known as demantoid has been found. Excellent crystals of epidote, clinozoisite, prehnite, pectolite, and many other minerals also have been found in rodingites.

Skarns and rodingites are not the only rocks formed by the action of chemically reactive fluids during metamorphism. The movement of hydrothermal solutions along contact zones between rocks of different com-

PLATE 131

Diopside (pale green) **with**
Clinochlore (micaceous green) **and**
Grossular (orange).
Mussa Alp, Piedmont, Italy.
3.5 x 4.5 cm.

The same tectonic forces that created the
Alps also mobilized hydrothermal solutions
to make these minerals and others in a belt
of serpentinite that stretches across
northern Italy into Austria.

PLATE 132

Charoite.
Chary River, northwest Aldan,
Yakut, Russia. 8 x 10 cm.

Complex reactions between alkalic rocks
and marble resulted in this attractive,
unique gem mineral.

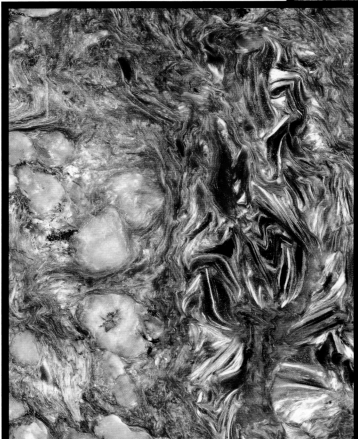

The Formation of Rodingites.

a. When plates collide, pieces of oceanic crust are sometimes thrust over continental crust. b. With time the oceanic crust may become incorporated into a mountain chain, as the plates continue to move. c. Granitic magma formed by melting sediments dragged down a subduction zone rises and intrudes the old slab of oceanic crust as dikes. d. Heat and pressure cause hydrothermal solutions to be driven from the rock. The solutions chemically alter the oceanic crustal rock (e.g., peridotite) into serpentinite and the granitic dikes into rodingites.

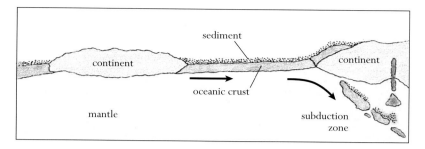

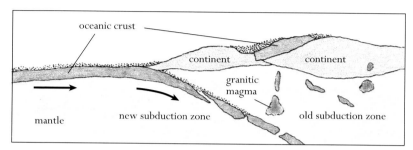

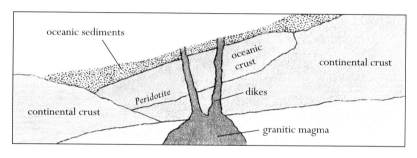

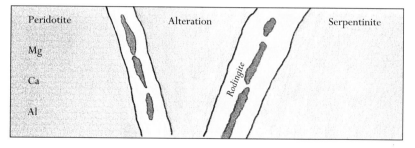

positions frequently results in the chemical alteration of one or both rocks. This type of alteration is especially evident in tectonically active areas such as folded mountain chains, where changes in temperature and pressure are experienced. The commercial deposits of talc in the Appalachians of Vermont and in southern Quebec probably formed in such a manner along contacts between serpentinite and various indigenous rocks, as did deposits of nephrite jade in similar geological settings. The huge almandine garnet crystals exposed at the Barton mine on Gore Mountain, near North Creek, New York, also are believed to be the result of chemical replacement along a contact zone, in this case between an olivine metagabbro and metasyenite. Charoite [PLATE 132] is found in chemically altered rocks at the contact of a nepheline aegirine syenite with limestone in the Chary River area, northwest Aldan, Yakut, Russia. Occurring as large masses of interlocking lavender crystals associated with several other rare minerals, charoite is used as both a gemstone and an ornamental rock. To date, the deposit remains unique ●

chapter thirty-two

Summary of Recrystallization

MANY minerals are not stable when exposed to high temperature and pressure and respond by reorganizing their own atoms into new, more-stable structures or by reacting chemically to form new minerals that are more stable under the prevailing conditions. This natural process of recycling old minerals into new ones is known as recrystallization. Recrystallization is facilitated by the presence of (usually water-rich) fluids in the rock, although the process itself occurs in the solid state. The metamorphic rocks that result are changed both chemically and physically. The parallel alignment of platy and rodlike minerals in response to directed pressure usually imparts a layered structure to these rocks. ❡ The three most important factors that determine which minerals form during recrystallization are temperature, pressure, and the chemical components available from the minerals and fluids in the rock. After metamorphism, rocks often show progressive zones of changing mineral assemblages that correlate with gradients in temperature and pressure. The presence of indicator minerals denotes specific conditions of temperature and pressure. The greater the number of chemical components involved, the greater the variety of minerals that may form. ❡ In more-complex systems, additional chemical components may be introduced by the intrusion of a magma or its accompanying diffusion. Since the area affected is confined to that in contact with the intrusion, the resulting process is called contact metamorphism. Within the contact zone, or aureole, there is usually evidence of chemical replacement of one mineral by another. Contact metamorphism is characterized by high temperature but relatively low pressure. Skarns are one of the most familiar examples of contact metamorphism, and result when a magma intrudes a carbonate-rich rock, such as limestone or dolostone. The carbonate rock supplies calcium, magnesium, and carbon dioxide to the system, while the magma supplies silicon, aluminum, iron, sodium, potassium, and various volatile components. The resulting skarn is thus rich in silicates of those elements. The presence of other minor chemical constituents enables numerous more exotic minerals to form. The conditions of contact metamorphism may be mimicked by other geological processes, such as the incorporation of pieces of limestone by a magma and their subsequent recrystallization under conditions of high temperature and low pressure.

Various geological settings may provide the conditions necessary for recrystallization. Both temperature and pressure increase as one progresses into the Earth's crust from its surface. Thus, simple burial of sediments in deep basins may be enough to initiate recrystallization. As sediments and oceanic crustal rocks are carried along the Earth's tectonic plates, they are also subjected to changes in heat and pressure. These changes are especially evident at plate boundaries, where plates collide. Hydrothermal fluids may be released by such tectonic activity and chemically alter the rocks they contact, making new minerals. Magnesium-rich rocks such as peridotites are often transformed into serpentinite during the process, while associated igneous rocks such as granite may be converted into rodingites. Rocks of dissimilar compositions also may be placed in contact with each other by activity along faults. Fluids migrating along their contact under the elevated temperatures and pressures of metamorphism may promote recrystallization. Numerous geological environments are conducive to recrystallization, each providing a mechanism for change in its governing parameters: temperature, pressure, and available chemical components ●

Summary

PART VI

of

Mineral-forming Processes

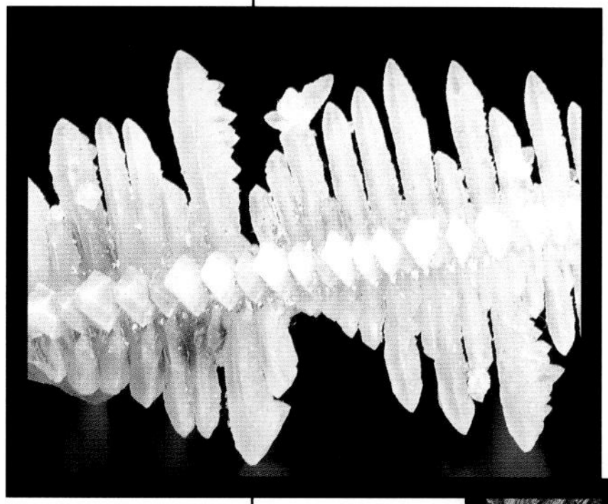

PLATE 133

Beryl, variety emerald.
Muzo, Colombia. 4-cm crystal.

Several mineral-forming processes were required to make this crystal of emerald.

PLATE 134

Cubanite.
Henderson mine, Chibougamau, Quebec. 3-cm crystal.

It is hard to believe that the iron, copper, and sulfur constituting these lustrous, rare crystals of cubanite were probably once a black cloud of sulfide "smoke" spewed from a hydrothermal vent kilometers beneath the ocean.

chapter thirty-three

Interaction of Mineral-forming

Processes

MINERALS are chemical compounds having specific ranges of stability with respect to physical and chemical factors such as heat, pressure, pH, and oxidation. These ranges are broad for some minerals, such as quartz and calcite, but narrow for others, such as diamond and gypsum. Often more than one geological environment provides conditions conducive to the formation of a particular mineral. That's why vivianite and other phosphate minerals may occur in such radically different geological settings as granitic pegmatites in Brazil or quartz veins in shale in northern Canada. More than one geological or mineral-forming process may be required to make some minerals. Nowhere is this better illustrated than in the famous emerald deposits of Colombia, or the volcanogenic massive sulfide deposits of the Canadian shield. ❧ The emerald mines of the Muzo and Chivor districts of Colombia have been actively worked since the mid-1500s, but only now are we beginning to understand how the deposits probably formed. A good part of the reason for our longstanding ignorance is that these deposits are totally unlike any other known occurrences of beryl, including other emeralds. Instead of occurring in granitic pegmatites or mica schists, emeralds in Colombia [PLATE 133] occur in veins of calcite and albite in black, organic-rich shales and limestones — sedimentary rocks normally indicative of relatively low temperatures and pressures. Even a few rare specimens of emerald replacing fossil snails have been found! Because all other occurrences of beryl are related to magmatic fluids, for years a similar origin was surmised for the solutions that deposited the Colombian emeralds. However, recent research offers a very different and plausible explanation. ❧ By studying the compositions and distribution of specific isotopes in fluid inclusions in these emeralds, we now know that the hydrothermal solution from which the emeralds crystallized does not have a magmatic origin at all. Instead it is more akin to a localized, higher-temperature version of a Mississippi Valley Type deposit. In MVT deposits metals are leached from sediments in geological basins by brines, which carry them in solution to their site of deposition. There chemical reactions (perhaps involving organic molecules) cause the metal-bearing minerals to precipitate.

In Colombia, tectonic forces deformed and fractured the organic-rich shale and limestone that hosts the emerald deposits, creating openings and releasing brines trapped in the sediments. The beryllium and other essential elements needed to form the emeralds were probably present in the sediments themselves and entered the brine complexed with organic molecules. As the somewhat acidic brine cooled in the fractures, it reacted with the limestone, which neutralized the brine and caused various minerals, including emeralds, to precipitate. The fortuitously present sulfur (probably in the form of hydrogen sulfide, H_2S) scavenged the available iron and precipitated it as pyrite, thereby preventing iron from being incorporated by the crystallizing emeralds. If that had happened, the color of the resulting beryl would probably have been a much more ordinary blue-green.

Volcanogenic massive sulfide deposits have an even more complex history. To see how some of these deposits form, we must journey to the bottom of the ocean where two of the Earth's plates are actively spreading apart, such as along the Mid-Atlantic or Juan de Fuca Ridges. Scientists traveling in deep-sea submersible vessels have visited both locations, collecting samples and recording their findings on videotape. In addition to witnessing underwater volcanic eruptions and discovering some new, interesting life forms, these scientists discovered and filmed a geological wonder that has revolutionized how geologists interpret the origins of many ore deposits: **black smokers.** Like smokestacks on a factory roof, these strange pipelike structures billow out clouds of what appears to be dense, black smoke, which, when analyzed, is found to be a very fine precipitate of sulfide minerals.

As seawater seeps down through cracks in the basaltic oceanic crust on the ocean floor, it is warmed by the magma below [FIGURE K]. The resulting hot, salty solution dissolves some of the metal-bearing minerals in the basalt. As if in a giant percolator, the solution is heated and forced back up through the cracks in the rock, dissolving more minerals, until ultimately it encounters the ice-cold seawater. Unable to remain in solution because of the abrupt change in temperature, the metals precipitate out as metal-sulfide minerals such as pyrite, chalcopyrite, galena, and sphalerite. The larger the chimneys grow, the more unstable they become, and eventually they topple over in a mound, but the finely dispersed sulfide "smoke" may spread out over a considerable area and settle as finely banded layers on the seafloor.

The finely dispersed sulfide minerals produced by black smokers are gradually buried by other marine sediments and carried away from their birthplace as the plates slowly drift apart. Eventually the sulfide-rich sediments reach a continent, where they are either carried downward along with the subsiding plate or are scraped off onto the continent. In the first case they descend toward the mantle and are heated until they melt, forming a sulfide-rich magma. Under pressure the

Volcanogenic Massive Sulfide
Deposits.

*a. Near mid-oceanic ridges where two
plates spread apart, magma heats
seawater, which infiltrates fractures in the
oceanic crust and dissolves metals from the
rock. The heated water is forced upward
under pressure and erupts from the seafloor
as what is known as a black smoker. The
"smoke" is really a fine precipitate of
sulfide minerals that settles to the bottom
as sediment. b. The sulfide-rich sediment is
carried by the moving plate to a continent,
where it may be scraped off and recrystallized into a massive sulfide deposit in a
forming folded mountain chain.
c. Alternatively, the sediment may be
carried down a subduction zone and
melted to form a sulfide-rich magma,
which rises and forms a massive sulfide
deposit by crystallization and segregation.*

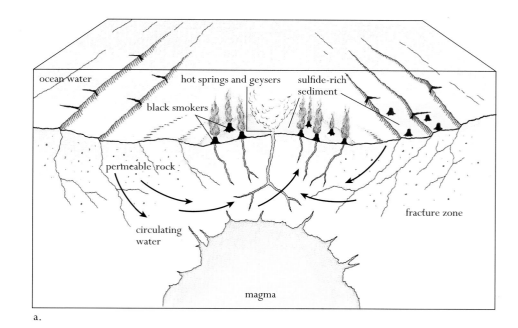

a.

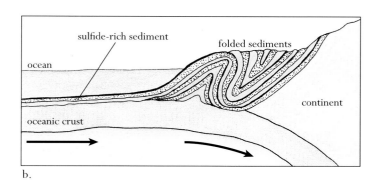

b.

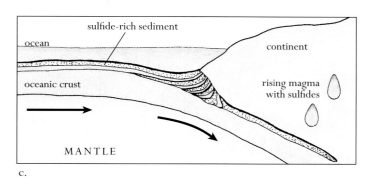

c.

magma rises along faults and fractures into the crust above it, where it eventually may form an ore deposit. In the second scenario, the sulfides are subjected to
substantial heat and pressure from the tremendous force exerted by the converging plates and are recrystallized. Continued tectonic activity causes the sulfides to be folded and fractured as they are uplifted and incorporated into a
forming mountain chain.

The fracturing also opens channels for tectonically activated hydrothermal
solutions to enter and precipitate a second generation of sulfides, locally enrich-
ing the grade of the ore. The cubanite crystals in plate 134 probably formed in
such a manner. As uplift continues, erosion wears down the rocks covering the
deposit, exposing it to the surface and providing some lucky prospector with an
opportunity to become a millionaire. Some of the world's richest mines are
thought to have formed in this way. The repeated association of such massive
sulfide deposits with volcanic rocks and marine sediments along both modern
and ancient continental margins is more than just coincidence; it's a consequence of the recycling of the Earth's minerals by plate tectonics●

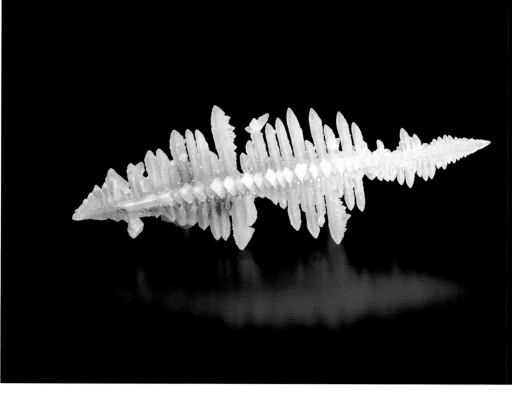

PLATE 135

Sulfur.

Perticara, Sicily, Italy. 3-cm crystals.

Once thought to be of volcanic origin, we now know that these crystals of sulfur formed by a biological process, as bacteria chemically converted the sulfate in minerals like anhydrite into elemental sulfur.

PLATE 136

Sal Ammoniac.

Ravat, Tadshikistan. 1.5 x 5 cm.

This type of skeletal crystal commonly results from rapid growth, which is characteristic of sublimation, the transition of a substance directly from a vapor to the solid state. In this case the vapor came from burning beds of coal.

chapter thirty-four

Biogenic Minerals

IN addition to the tectonic forces that recycle rocks and make minerals, we must reckon with another "force," the rather incredible "geological force" of life itself. In Part IV I gave examples of how oxidation-reduction reactions govern the genesis of certain minerals. Another very interesting, though less obvious, variant of such reactions—that provided by certain microorganisms—also leads to the formation of minerals. Plants and animals have respiratory systems that oxidize food aerobically (i.e., using oxygen) to produce energy. Anaerobic bacteria, however, do not have this capability. They derive their energy by the process of **chemosynthesis.** ❡ Anaerobic bacteria can take advantage of elements with multiple oxidation states, such as iron and sulfur, by effecting a change in the oxidation state. The energy released in the process sustains the life of the bacteria. For example, some bacteria can oxidize native sulfur or sulfide-bearing minerals into sulfates. The reverse process is accomplished by other bacteria, which reduce sulfates to sulfides. The white staining frequently seen on old limestone or concrete buildings is a result of the first of these reactions. Sulfate produced by bacteria oxidizing sulfides in the limestone reacts with calcium in the limestone or concrete to make gypsum (calcium sulfate), which forms the powdery white coating. The products of sulfur-reducing bacteria commonly occur as pyrite or other sulfide minerals in dark, organic-rich shales [see PLATE 78]. Because the genesis of such minerals is biologically driven, they are said to have a **biogenic** origin. ❡ Another, and economically more important, example of a biogenic mineral is native sulfur itself [PLATE 135]. Once thought to be of volcanic origin, most of the world's major sulfur deposits, such as those in Poland, in Sicily, or

along the Gulf coast of the southeastern United States, are now known to have been created by sulfate reduction by microorganisms. The biogenic origin of native sulfur was determined using isotope analysis. The most abundant isotope of sulfur is ^{32}S, but ^{34}S is also relatively common. Bacteria preferentially act on the lighter ^{32}S isotope, which causes a relative increase in the concentration of the heavier isotope, ^{34}S, in the "unused" sulfate. By measuring the concentrations of these two isotopes in the sulfur and sulfate, we can establish whether or not the reaction has been driven by bacteria.

In the Sicilian sulfur deposits, it is believed that beds of gypsum and anhydrite (both calcium sulfates) provided the sulfate that was reduced to sulfide (probably in the form of H_2S) while organic material was oxidized, liberating carbon dioxide. The carbon dioxide dissolved in water, forming carbonic acid (H_2CO_3), which reacted with the calcium ions derived from the gypsum and anhydrite to form aragonite or calcite (both $CaCO_3$). The frequent presence of hydrocarbons in close association with all these minerals lends credence to the theory that they are biogenic.

The crystals of sulfur, sal ammoniac [PLATE 136], and other minerals from Ravat, Tadshikistan, have different biological roots. These minerals form from vapors given off by burning beds of coal below the Earth's surface. Following fractures to the surface, the vapors cool rapidly, and the minerals form by **sublimation** (i.e., crystallization from a vapor directly to a solid). Certain calcium phosphate minerals (e.g., hydroxlapatite, monetite or brushite) are thought to derive their phosphorus from accumulations of bird droppings (called guano) from the large colonies of birds that inhabit some coral islands. The droppings are a source of soluble phosphorus that reacts with the calcium carbonate in the underlying coral to produce these minerals.

Similar reactions are known to occur in limestone caves that contain large accumulations of bat excrement (also called guano). Iron and aluminum phosphates such as strengite, phosphosiderite, and variscite have been found in guano deposits where iron- or aluminum-rich minerals are present beneath the droppings. Near Kerch, on the Crimean peninsula of Ukraine, well-formed crystals of vivianite and anapaite occur in casts of fossil shells [PLATE 137]. Vivianite occurs with other phosphate species in fossil shells at Mullica Hill, New Jersey, and the large crystals of vivianite found in clay in Richmond, Virginia, in the 1960s were reported to have been associated with fossilized whale bones.

Microorganisms are not the only life forms responsible for biogenic minerals. Interference in geological systems by fungi, plants, and animals—including humans—also causes minerals to form. The ancient mines of Laurium, Greece, located on the Aegean Sea approximately 40 kilometers southeast of Athens, have been worked for lead, silver, and zinc since 600 B.C. Slag produced from smelting the ore was dumped into the sea, where unrecovered lead reacted with seawater to form laurionite, penfieldite, and other rare minerals in cavities created by gas bubbles in the slag. All sorts of secondary sulfate minerals form on the walls of mines, where mining operations

PLATE 137

Anapaite.
Kerch Peninsula, Crimea, Ukraine.
4 x 5 cm.

Did the dissolution of the fossil shells lead to the formation of this specimen of anapaite by providing the necessary calcium or by locally changing the pH to a range more favorable for anapaite to form?

Cuprite on Copper.
Britannia mine, Britannia Beach,
British Columbia. 9 x 17 cm.

*Are these minerals? The copper
precipitated from water flowing over an
iron pipe unintentionally left behind in
the process of mining. The cuprite formed
naturally by reacting with oxygen from the
air, just as it probably did to form the
crystals in PLATE 80.*

have exposed primary sulfide minerals to moisture and air. Without human intervention, none of these minerals would have formed where they did.

As we drive down the highway in our cars and trucks, exhaust contaminated with lead from gasoline additives settles onto the roadside, where it reacts with phosphates in the soil to make plumbogummite. And how many kinds of minerals do you suppose might eventually form in our landfills and garbage dumps? Will any of them become an ore body? Even within our own bodies mineral processes are at work. Hydroxylapatite forms an essential part of our bones and teeth, and the less fortunate among us may be manufacturing struvite or weddellite in the form of urinary stones.

The formation of minerals by biogenic processes presents mineralogists with a philosophical problem: when is a mineral not a mineral? There are probably as many definitions of minerals as there are textbooks about them, but all the definitions have some common criteria: minerals must occur naturally, be a solid phase, and have a definite chemical composition and crystal structure. Some definitions also include caveats that minerals must be inorganic or be formed by inorganic processes. Hence purists may question the validity of biogenic or post-mining products [PLATE 138] as mineral species. Even most purists, however, have a hard time accepting that imposing such a rigid definition excludes such classic examples as the sulfur crystals from Sicily, the calcite forming the chalk in the white cliffs of Dover, England, and perhaps all marine dolomite from minerals.

Where human activities result in the formation of minerals, we must consider intent. If the intent of the activity is to produce the species (e.g., a furnace-grown diamond or ruby), then most mineralogists would probably consider it a synthetic compound, not a mineral. By this definition, the biogenic aragonite constituting a natural pearl would be considered a mineral, but the same compound in a cultured pearl would not because, without deliberate human intervention, the oyster would not have produced the pearl●

chapter thirty-five

What Have We Learned?

Y OU now know that some minerals form by a single process, others by several. You have also seen that considerable overlap and interaction may exist between these processes and the forces (including life!) that drive them. My decision to include or exclude any given mineral from the discussion of the main geological processes has been arbitrary and, of course, is limited by how much scientists know about its genesis. Often I can attribute the genesis of a mineral to a particular mineral-forming process with confidence based on its physical structure, associated species, or analogy to similar specimens of known origins. These conclusions usually are correct, but they may be wrong, especially if extended too far. ❡ For example I am confident that the famous rhodochrosite stalactites from Catamarca Province, Argentina [PLATE 139], form in open voids by precipitation from aqueous solutions because all other stalactites form in that way and because rhodochrosite is common in deposits of hydrothermal origin. I am not comfortable, though, speculating on whether the source of the aqueous solution that formed these specimens is meteoric, magmatic, or tectonic because I have never visited this locality, performed any fluid-inclusion or isotope studies on the rhodochrosite, or read an account of such studies. Similarly, I believe that the famous large stibnite crystals from the Ichinokawa mine on the island of Shikoku, Japan, as well as the classic examples of wire silver from Kongsberg, Norway [PLATE 140], also formed by precipitation from aqueous solutions, but I can only guess about the source of the antimony or silver required to make these minerals, or about the derivation of the solutions. ❡ The twentieth century has seen incredible advances in science and technology, ranging from humankind's first powered

PLATE 139

Rhodochrosite.
Catamarca, Argentina. 6 x 8.5 cm.

Its formation by precipitation from aqueous solution may be inferred from the structure of this rhodochrosite stalactite, but the sources for the solution or the manganese and carbonate it must have contained cannot.

PLATE 140

Wire Silver.
Kongsberg, Norway. 8 x 10 cm.

Although this silver specimen is from one of the world's most famous mineral localities and silver mining districts, many of the specifics concerning its origin remain a mystery.

flight to its first footsteps on the moon. By understanding how minerals form in nature, we are now able to synthesize many of them and can even improve some of their desired properties by doing so. We have made great strides in understanding how nature operates, but as each new discovery answers a question, it nearly always raises numerous others. We have gained considerable knowledge of how matter behaves in relatively simple, closed systems, and from the laws of thermodynamics we can successfully predict which minerals should be stable at a given set of parameters for that system. Unfortunately, nature seldom provides such simple, closed systems. A quick look at the silicon-oxygen system proves the point.

Silica (SiO_2) may appear as one of several different minerals, depending on temperature and pressure. At atmospheric pressure, low quartz, high quartz, tridymite, and cristobalite crystallize at progressively higher temperatures. At significantly higher pressures, coesite or stishovite may form. (The existence of the latter two species was predicted before their actual discovery in nature.) At the Earth's surface, low quartz is the stable form of SiO_2. Tridymite should exist only at temperatures from 870 to 1470°C, yet tridymite still persists in volcanic rocks formed in that temperature range at the Earth's surface tens of thousands of years ago, because it lacks the activation energy required to recrystallize into low quartz.

Opal, another silica-rich mineral, forms under near-atmospheric conditions of low pressure and temperature and should therefore form as low quartz. X-ray studies of opal indicate, however, that the much-higher-temperature mineral cristobalite, is the species usually present. How can this be? The answer is that although they are SiO_2, the opals formed in a complex system containing more than just silicon and oxygen. The system includes water, aluminum, and alkali metals, which, when incorporated in only minor amounts into the structure of the crystallizing SiO_2, favor a cristobalite-like structure.

The world of mineralogy is full of surprises and unanswered questions. Knowing positively how a given mineral has formed and why is the exception rather than the rule. Because minerals and the elements they contain have become essential to our everyday lives, research will undoubtedly continue to reveal new information about their properties, potential uses, and formation in nature. Knowledge of how minerals form is fundamental to locating future ore deposits and to synthesizing substitutes for crucial minerals whose natural occurrences are being depleted. *Homo sapiens* is in a unique position: no other organism has such an ability to understand and control its environment. Understanding the Earth's basic geological processes and their relationship with the biosphere and with human activity is essential to our own survival ●

Recommended Reading

American Geological Institute. 1962. *Dictionary of Geological Terms.* Garden City, NY: Dolphin Books, Doubleday. A concise, handy reference for all audiences.

Bancroft, Peter. 1973. *The World's Finest Minerals and Crystals.* New York: Viking Press. Intended primarily for mineral collectors, this is an easily read text.

Bancroft, Peter. 1984. *Gem and Crystal Treasures.* Fallbrook, CA: Western Enterprises. A unique blend of travel, history, and descriptive mineralogy focusing on most of the world's most important mineral localities; for both general and informed audiences.

Brownlow, Arthur H. 1979. *Geochemistry.* Englewood Cliffs, NJ: Prentice-Hall, 1979. A modern, broad-based approach to geochemistry for an advanced audience.

Carmichael, Ian S. E., Francis J. Turner, and John Verhoogen. 1974. *Igneous Petrology.* New York: McGraw-Hill. A thorough discussion of magmatic processes and the genesis of igneous rocks; advanced level.

Cattermole, Peter, and Patrick Moore. 1985. *The Story of the Earth.* Cambridge: Cambridge University Press. A modern physical geology text written for a general or informed audience.

Cocks, L. R. M., and P. H. Greenwood, eds. 1981. *Chance, Change and Challenge: The Evolving Earth.* Cambridge: Cambridge University Press. A compendium of papers on the evolution of the Earth and its geological systems; for an informed audience.

Degens, Egon T. 1989. *Perspectives on Biogeochemistry.* New York: Springer-Verlag. A comprehensive review of the interaction between the living and nonliving world; advanced level.

Desautels, Paul E. 1968. *The Mineral Kingdom.* New York: Madison Square Press, Grosset and Dunlap. A nontechnical approach to the fascinating world of minerals; written for a general audience.

Ehrlich, Henry Lutz. 1981. *Geomicrobiology.* New York: Marcel Dekker. A technical discussion of some of the more important biogenic minerals; advanced level.

Fleischer, Michael, and Joseph A. Mandarino. 1991. *Glossary of Mineral Species 1991.* Tucson: The Mineralogical Record. A handy, alphabetical listing giving the chemical formula and a published reference for all known mineral species.

Frye, Keith, ed. 1981. *The Encyclopedia of Mineralogy.* Stroudsburg, PA: Hutchinson Ross. A comprehensive, advanced reference manual.

Guilbert, John M., and Charles F. Park, Jr. 1986. *The Geology of Ore Deposits.* New York: W. H. Freeman. A comprehensive review explaining the genesis of nearly every kind of ore deposit; intended for an informed to advanced audience.

Jackson, Kern C. 1970. *Textbook of Lithology.* New York: McGraw-Hill. A thorough treatment of the fundamentals of physical geology for a general but informed audience.

Kearey, Philip, ed. 1993. *The Encyclopedia of the Solid Earth Sciences.* Oxford: Blackwell Scientific Publications. A modern, comprehensive reference manual for all audiences.

Keller, Peter C. 1990. *Gemstones and Their Origins.* New York: Van Nostrand Reinhold. An informative, well-illustrated text explaining the genesis of some of the world's most important gem deposits; for both general and informed audiences.

Lapedes, Daniel N., ed. 1978. *McGraw-Hill Encyclopedia of the Geological Sciences.* New York: McGraw-Hill. A comprehensive reference manual for all audiences.

Mason, Brian. 1958. *Principles of Geochemistry.* New York: John Wiley and Sons. One of the classic texts describing the chemistry of the Earth and its geological processes; for an advanced audience.

Mason, Brian, and L. G. Berry. 1968. *Elements of Mineralogy.* San Francisco: W. H. Freeman. A traditional but popular mineralogy textbook; for an informed audience.

Mottana, Annibale, Rodolfo Crespi, and Giuseppe Liborio. 1978. *Guide to Rocks and Minerals.* New York: Simon and Schuster. A handy pictorial guide for a general or informed audience.

Nickel, Ernest H., and Monte C. Nichols. 1991. *Mineral Reference Manual.* New York: Van Nostrand Reinhold. A handy, alphabetical listing giving chemical and physical data with reference citations for all known mineral species.

Pough, Frederick H. 1960. *A Field Guide to Rocks and Minerals.* Boston: Houghton Mifflin. One of the most popular texts among amateur mineralogists; for general and informed audiences.

Redfern, Ron. 1983. *The Making of a Continent.* New York: Times Books, New York Times Book Company. A well-illustrated text explaining the principles of plate tectonics; for general to informed audiences.

Roberts, Willard Lincoln, Thomas J. Campbell, and George Robert Rapp, Jr. 1990. *Encyclopedia of Minerals.* 2d ed. New York: Van Nostrand Reinhold. A comprehensive reference manual for all audiences.

Sinkankas, John. 1964. *Mineralogy for Amateurs.* New York: Van Nostrand Reinhold. A comprehensive, easily read, popular text for general and informed audiences.

Sofianides, Anna S., and George E. Harlow. 1990. *Gems and Crystals from the American Museum of Natural History.* New York: Simon and Schuster. A well-illustrated, easily read text focusing on the occurrence, properties, history, and lore of common and uncommon gemstones; for general or informed audiences.

Strahler, Arthur N. 1981. *Physical Geology.* New York: Harper and Row. A thorough treatment of the fundamentals of physical geology for a general but informed audience.

Tindall, James R., and Roger Thornhill. 1975. *The Collector's Guide to Rocks and Minerals.* New York: Van Nostrand Reinhold. An easily read text intended for a general audience.

Turner, Francis J. 1968. *Metamorphic Petrology: Mineralogical and Field Aspects.* New York: McGraw-Hill. A thorough, advanced discussion of metamorphism and metamorphic rocks.

Verhoogen, John, Francis J. Turner, Lionel E. Weiss, and Clyde Wahrhaftig. 1970. *The Earth: An Introduction to Physical Geology.* New York: Holt, Rinehart and Winston. A comprehensive, advanced physical geology text.

Wilk, Harry, and Olaf Medenbach. 1986. *The Magic of Minerals.* New York: Springer-Verlag. Superb photographs highlight this introduction to the world of minerals; for general and informed audiences.

Winkler, Helmut G. F. 1979. *Petrogenesis of Metamorphic Rocks.* 5th ed. New York: Springer-Verlag. A thorough, advanced discussion of metamorphism and metamorphic rocks.

Appendix: Some Additional Minerals and How They Form

There are currently about 3,800 known mineral species. In selecting those discussed in the preceding chapters, I have tried to strike a balance between minerals and localities that are familiar, and those that best illustrate a particular geological process. As a result, some important minerals had to be omitted, along with many additional examples of ways that given species might form. The following table lists some of these minerals, their localities, and modes of genesis. Although some, such as carletonite or cumengite, are globally rare species, they have been included because they are often seen in collections. I have used general mineral names to imply a series of species, especially when the species have common modes of origin (e.g., "allanite" implies allanite-(Ce) and allanite-(Y); "axinite" implies ferro-, magnesio-, or manganaxinite). Similarly, polymorphs with similar modes of origin, such as atacamite and paratacamite, have been listed simply as "atacamite." The process/type code used in the table is given below, and the numbered references follow the table. Where possible, I have tried to provide nontechnical references that describe the occurrence of the species and its associated minerals. References giving more complete and scientific descriptions for each species may be found in the *Encyclopedia of Minerals, Mineral Reference Manual,* and *Glossary of Mineral Species,* which are cited in the Recommended Reading list. A visit to nearly any university or museum library will provide many more.

....

Processes and Types

M	· crystallization from magma		C	· chemical alteration
ag	· agpaitic pegmatite		bi	· biogenic
cb	· carbonatite		ox	· oxidation-reduction
df	· differentiation		re	· chemical replacement
gr	· granitic pegmatite		hp	· hydrothermal alteration in
vx	· volcanic extrusive			pegmatite
P	· precipitation from aqueous solution		R	· recrystallization
al	· alpine cleft		rd	· rodingite
ev	· evaporite		rm	· regional metamorphism
mvt	· Mississippi Valley type		sk	· skarn
mt	· meteoric		cm	· contact metamorphism
hy	· hydrothermal (mg · magmatic,		vs	· recrystallized volcanogenic
	me · meteoric, tc · tectonic,			massive sulfide deposit
	bs · basalt flow mineralization)			

....

Species	Locality	Process/type	References
Acanthite	Cobalt, Ontario	P/hy	14,78,148
	Freiberg, Saxony, Germany	P/hy-mg	5,6,121,180,202
	Guanajuato, Mexico	P/hy	6,151,202
Andorite	Oruro, Bolivia	P/hy-mg	5,32,202
Ajoite	Ajo, Arizona	C/ox	194
	Messina District, South Africa	C/ox	21
Allanite	Madawaska, Ontario	M/gr	171
	Fahlun, Sweden	M/gr	42,212
	Olden Twp., Frontenac County, Ontario	R/cm	171
	Otter Lake, Quebec	R/cm	115
	Trimouns, France	P/al	173
	Eifel District, Germany	M/vx	83
Alstonite	Alston, Cumbria, England	P/mvt + C?	149
	Hardin County, Illinois	P/mvt + C?	122,177

Species	Locality	Process/type	References
Anhydrite	Naica, Chihuahua, Mexico	P/hy	151
	Simplon Tunnel, Switzerland	P/al	5,149,203
	Stassfurt, Saxony, Germany	P/ev	19,149
Annabergite	Laurium, Greece	C/ox	105
Anthophyllite-gedrite	Fiskenaesset, Greenland	R/rm	159
	Nuuk, Greenland	R/rm	2
Antlerite	Chiquicamata, Chile	C/ox	33,149
Artinite	Staten Island, New York	P/hy-tc?	91,167
	San Benito County, California	P/hy-tc	31
Astrophyllite	St. Peters Dome, Colorado	M/ag	140,152
	Mont Saint-Hilaire, Quebec	M/ag	85,125
	Narssârssuk, Greenland	M/ag	159
Atacamite	Wallaroo, South Australia	C-ox	162
	Atacama, Chile	C-ox	33
Augelite	North Groton, New Hampshire	C/hp	135,184
	Rapid Creek, Yukon Territory	P/hy-tc	176
	Oruro, Bolivia	P/hy-mg	32
	Mono County, California	P/hy	223
Augite	Salzburg, Austria	P/al	6,183
	Ariccia, Roma, Italy	M/df	42
	Franklin, New Jersey	R/sk	58,59,146
	Eifel District, Germany	M/vx	83
Austinite	Gold Hill, Utah	C/ox	106
	Mapimi, Durango, Mexico	C/ox	151
Autunite	Spokane, Washington	C/ox	166
	Autun, Saône-et-Loire, France	C/ox	149
Axinite	Bourg d'Oisans, Isère, France	P/al	49
	New Melones Lake, California	P/al	160
	Polar Urals, Russia	P/hy-tc	185
	Luning, Nevada	R/sk?	49
	Bungo Province, Kyushu, Japan	R/cm	181
	Vitória da Conquista, Bahia, Brazil	P/hy-tc	25
Babingtonite	Westfield, Massachusetts	P/hy-bs	147
	Bombay, Maharashtra, India	P/hy-bs	40
	Paterson, New Jersey	P/hy-bs	156,157
Beryllonite	Stoneham, Maine	C/hp?	135,155
	Paprok, Nuristan, Afghanistan	C/hp?	175
Betafite	Betafo area, Madagascar	M/gr	148
	Bancroft, Ontario	R/sk (M/cb?)	102,171
Bismuthinite	Jefferson County, Colorado	M/gr	148
	Cornwall, England	P/hy-mg	52,148
	Kingsgate, New South Wales Australia	P/hy-mg	53
Blödite	Soda Lake, California	P/ev	154
Boleite	Boleo, Baja California, Mexico	C/ox	6,151
Boracite	Lüneburg, Hannover, Germany	P/ev	19,149
Boulangerite	Noche Buena, Zacatecas, Mexico	P/hy	151
	Trepca, Serbia	P/hy	120
	Madoc, Ontario	P/hy-me?	16,130
Brazilianite	Minas Gerais, Brazil	C/hp	5,6,135
	North Groton, New Hampshire	C/hp	41,135,184
	Rapid Creek, Yukon Territory	P/hy-tc	176
Brewsterite	Strontian, Scotland	P/hy	196
	Yellow Lake, British Columbia	P/hy-bs	196
	Harrisville, New York	P/hy-tc	172

Species	Locality	Process/type	References
Brochantite	Bisbee, Arizona	C/ox	68
	Bingham, New Mexico	C/ox	192
Brucite	Brewster, New York	P/hy-tc	88,91
	Texas, Pennsylvania	P/hy-tc	63,148
	Asbest, Russia	R/rd	174
	Asbestos, Quebec	R/rd	77
Buergerite	San Luis Potosi, Mexico	M/vx	47,151
Cacoxenite	Hagendorf, Bavaria, Germany	C/hp	135
	Indian Mountain, Alabama	P/mt	12,67
	Coon Creek, Arkansas	P/mt	103
Calaverite	Cripple Creek, Colorado	P/hy-mg	6,187,217
	Calaveras County, California	P/hy	154,217
Caledonite	Tiger, Arizona	C/ox	6,17
	San Bernardino County, California	C/ox	39
	Leadhills, Lanarkshire, Scotland	C/ox	64
Cancrinite	Bancroft area, Ontario	C/re	84
	Mont Saint-Hilaire, Quebec	M/ag	85,125
	Eifel District, Germany	M/vx	83
	Point of Rocks, New Mexico	M/vx	43
Carletonite	Mont Saint-Hilaire, Quebec	R/cm	85,125
Carnotite	Colorado Plateau area, Utah, Colorado, New Mexico, Arizona	C/ox	78,149
Cavansite	Owyhee Dam, Malheur County, Oregon	P/hy-bs	208
	Poona, Maharashtra, India	P/hy-bs	111
Chondrodite	Amity, New York	R/rm	99
	Brewster, New York	R/sk	88,91
Chlorargyrite	Broken Hill, New South Wales, Australia	C/ox	127,224
Cinnabar	Almaden, Ciudad Real, Spain	P/hy	37
	Hunan & Kweichow Prov., China	P/hy	5,6,168,181
	Coast Range, California	P/hy	154
	Idria, Slovenia	P/hy-mg	7
Clinoclase	Tintic District, Utah	C/ox	126,149
	Liskeard, Cornwall, England	C/ox	52
	Majuba Hill, Nevada	C/ox	92,93
Cobaltite	Cobalt, Ontario	P/hy	14,78
	Tunaberg & Håkansboda, Sweden	R/sk	1,6
Conichalcite	Mapimi, Durango, Mexico	C/ox	151
	Gold Hill, Utah	C/ox	106
Covellite	Butte, Montana	P/hy-mg	6,148
	Summitville, Colorado	P/hy-mg	109
	Alghero, Sardinia, Italy	P/hy	148
Creedite	Santa Eulalia, Chihuahua, Mexico	P/hy	6,151
Cryolite	Ivigtut, Greenland	M/gr	6,159
	Mont Saint-Hilaire, Quebec	M/ag	85,125
	Francon quarry, Montreal, Quebec	M/cb	29
Cumengite	Boleo, Baja California, Mexico	C/ox	6,151
Cyanotrichite	Grand Canyon, Arizona	C/ox	117
	Moldawa, Banat, Romania	C/ox	149
Danburite	San Luis Potosi, Mexico	P/hy	151
	Russell, New York	R/sk	91
	Anjanabonoina, Madagascar	M/gr	221

Species	Locality	Process/type	References
Dawsonite	Francon quarry, Montreal, Quebec	M/cb	29
	Mte. Amiata, Tuscany, Italy	P/hy	149
	Mont Saint-Hilaire, Quebec	M/ag	85,125
Descloizite	Grootfontein, Namibia	C/ox	215
	Santa Eulalia, Chihuahua, Mexico	C/ox	151
Diaspore	Chester, Massachusetts	P/hy-tc	123
	Mugla Province, Turkey	P/hy-tc	136
Dresserite	Francon quarry, Montreal, Quebec	M/cb	29
Dumortierite	Alpine, California	R/rm	154
Dyscrasite	St. Andreasberg, Harz, Germany	P/hy-mg	6,121,148
	Príbram, Czech Republic	P/hy-mg	6,107
Edingtonite	Bathurst, New Brunswick	P/hy-tc	76
	Dumbartonshire, Scotland	P/hy-bs	196
	Ice River, British Columbia	M/ag	74
Enargite	Butte, Montana	P/hy-mg	6,148
	San Juan County, Colorado	P/hy-mg?	109,141
	Quiruvilca, La Libertad, Peru	P/hy-mg	118
Enstatite (Hypersthene)	Jackson County, No. Carolina	M/df	222
	North Creek, New York	R/rm	66,91
	Eifel District, Germany	M/vx	83
	Summit Rock, Oregon	M/vx	82
Epistilbite	Berufjord, Iceland	P/hy-bs	196
	Bombay, Maharashtra, India	P/hy-bs	40,196
Euxenite	Quadeville, Ontario	M/gr	102,171
	Madawaska, Ontario	M/gr	171
	Ampangabe, Madagascar	M/gr	148
	Iveland, Aust-Agder, Norway	M/gr	148,212
Fergusonite	Madawaska, Ontario	M/gr	102,171
	Iveland, Aust-Agder, Norway	M/gr	212
	Baringer Hill, Llano County, Texas	M/gr	186
Forsterite	Zabargad Island, Egypt	P/hy-me + C	6,100,214
	Notre-Dame-du-Laus, Quebec	R/cm	198
Francevillite	Mounana, Gabon	C/ox	28
Gadolinite	Falun, Sweden	M/gr	42,212
	Hiterö, Vest-Agder, Norway	M/gr	42,212
	Brunet & Llano Counties, Texas	M/gr	38,186
	Graubünden, Switzerland	P/al	70
Gahnite	Rowe, Massachusetts	R/rm	42
	Topsham, Maine	M/gr	57
	Franklin, New Jersey	R/sk	58,59,146
Glauberite	Camp Verde, Arizona	P/ev	195
	Searles Lake, California	P/ev	153,154
Glaucophane	Coast Range, California	R/rm	154
Gmelinite	Two Islands, Nova Scotia	P/hy-bs	196
	Flinders, Victoria, Australia	P/hy-bs	18,196
	Paterson, New Jersey	P/hy-bs	156,157,196
Gormanite - souzalite	Rapid Creek, Yukon Territory	P/hy-tc	176
Goyazite	Minas Gerais, Brazil	C/hp	135
	North Groton, New Hampshire	C/hp	135,184
	Rapid Creek, Yukon Territory	P/hy-tc	176
	Binnental, Valais, Switzerland	P/hy-tc	6,69,188
Graftonite	Grafton, New Hampshire	M/gr	41,135
	Black Hills, South Dakota	M/gr	135,170
Graphite	Ticonderoga, New York	R/cm	91,114
	Sri Lanka	R/rm	148
	Crestmore, California	R/sk	89

Species	Locality	Process/type	References
Greenockite	Bishopton, Renfrew, Scotland	P/hy	148
	Granby, Missouri	P/mvt	148
	Paterson, New Jersey	P/hy-bs	156,157
	Llallagua, Potosi, Bolivia	P/hy-mg	6,8
Gyrolite	Poona, Maharashtra, India	P/hy-bs	40
Halotrichite	Mojave, California	C/ox	154
Hambergite	San Diego County, California	M/gr	54,112
	Anjanabonoina, Madagascar	M/gr	219
	Gilgit, Pakistan	M/gr	98
Hanksite	Searles Lake, California	P/ev	153,154
Harmotome	Strontian, Scotland	P/hy	196
	Andreasberg, Harz, Germany	P/hy	196
	Vaasa, Finland	P/hy	196
Hauerite	Raddusa, Sicily, Italy	P/mt + C/bi?	5,148
Hauyne	Eifel District, Germany	M/df	83
	Mte. Somma, Vesuvius, Italy	M/df	42
Hessite	Botes, Transylvania, Romania	P/hy-mg	6,148
Hornblende	Aussig, Bohemia, Czech Republic	M/df	42
	Lake Harbour, Northwest Territories	R/sk	75
	Cornopass, Switzerland	R/rm	203
	Eifel District, Germany	M/vx	83
	Summit Rock, Oregon	M/vx	82
Howlite	Windsor & Iona, Nova Scotia	P/ev	97
	Boron, California	P/ev	3,4,6,139,163
Huebnerite	Pasto Bueno, Peru	P/hy-mg	6
	San Juan County, Colorado	P/hy-mg?	109,141
	Alpine County, California	P/hy	161
Hureaulite	Minas Gerais, Brazil	C/hp	50,135
	Black Hills, South Dakota	C/hp	135,170
	Mangualde, Beira, Portugal	C/hp	135
Hutchinsonite	Quiruvilca, La Libertad, Peru	P/hy-mg	118,210
	Binnental, Valais, Switzerland	P/hy-tc	6,69,188
Hyalophane	Busovaca, Bosnia	P/al	225
	Binnental, Valais, Switzerland	P/hy-tc	6,69,188
Hydromagnesite	Staten Island, New York	P/hy-tc?	91,167
	Soghan mine, Kerman, Iran	P/hy-tc?	9
Hydrozincite	Mapimi, Durango, Mexico	C/ox	151
	Goodsprings, Nevada	C/ox	149
Ilvaite	South Mountain, Idaho	R/sk	165,204
	Seriphos, Greece	R/sk	61,204
	Elba, Italy	R/sk	204
Inesite	Trinity County, California	P/hy	51,154
	Kuruman District, Cape Province, South Africa	P/hy	79,200,220
Iron	Disko Island, Greenland	M + C/ox	148,159
Jadeite	Tawmaw, Burma	R/rm & C	100
	San Benito County, California	R/rm & C	100
Jamesonite	Noche Buena & Nieves, Zacatecas, Mexico	P/hy	151
	Wolfsberg, Harz, Germany	P/hy	148
Jeremejevite	Swakapmund, Namibia	M/gr	209
	Mt. Soktuj, Siberia, Russia	M/gr	181
Kernite	Kern County, California	P/ev	3,4,6,139,163
Kinoite	Christmas, Arizona	C/ox	221
Kornerupine	Harts Range, Northern Territory, Australia	R/rm	128
	Fiskenaesset, Greenland	R/rm	158,159
	Betroka, Tulear, Madagascar	R/rm	42
Kröhnkite	Chuquicamata, Chile	C/ox	33
Kulanite	Rapid Creek, Yukon Territory	P/hy-tc	176
Laumontite	Bombay, Maharashtra, India	P/hy-bs	40,196
	Paterson, New Jersey	P/hy-bs	156,157,196
	Minas Basin, Nova Scotia	P/hy-bs	196
	Bishop, California	P/hy	144,154
Lawsonite	Tiburon Peninsula, California	R/rm	154
Lazulite	North Groton, New Hampshire	C/hp	135,184
	Minas Gerais, Brazil	C/hp	135
	Rapid Creek, Yukon Territory	P/hy-tc	176
	Werfen, Salzburg, Austria	P/hy-tc	142,149
	White Mountains, California	P/hy	223
	Graves Mountain, Georgia	R/rm	35
Lead	Långban, Sweden	P/hy	134,148
Leadhillite	Granby, Missouri	C/ox	149
	Tsumeb, Namibia	C/ox	215
	Leadhills, Scotland	C/ox	64
Levyne	Spray, Oregon	P/hy-bs	196
	Faeroe Islands	P/hy-bs	15,196
Libethenite	Cornwall, England	C/ox	52
	Mindola, Kitwe, Zambia	C/ox	108
	Libethen, Slovakia	C/ox	149
Liddicoatite	Antsirabe, Madagascar	M/gr	6,219
Linarite	Red Gill, Cumbria, England	C/ox	36
	Graham County, Arizona	C/ox	96
	Bingham, New Mexico	C/ox	192
Ludlamite	Rapid Creek, Yukon Teritory	P/hy-tc	176
	Cobalt, Idaho	P/hy	165
	North Groton, New Hampshire	C/hp	135,184
	Municipio de Aquiles Serdán, Chihuahua, Mexico	P/hy	6,151
Magnetite	Balmat, New York	P/hy	30
	Chester, Vermont	R/rm	71
	French Creek, Pennsylvania	R/sk	63
	Bancroft, Ontario	R/cm	171
	Eifel District, Germany	M/vx	83
	Mineville, New York	M/df	91
	St. Gotthard Pass, Switzerland	P/al	5,203
Margarite	Chester, Massachusetts	P/hy-tc	123
Mercury	Almaden, Ciudad Real, Spain	P/hy	37
	Sonoma & Sanata Clara Counties, California	P/hy	154
	Idria, Slovenia	P/hy-mg	7
Microlite	Amelia Courthouse, Virginia	M/gr	133
	Minas Gerais, Brazil	M/gr	27
Milarite	Val Guif, Grisons, Switzerland	P/al	203
	Jaguaraçu, Minas Gerais, Brazil	M/gr	216
	Gunanajuato, Mexico	P/hy	6,151
Millerite	Halls Gap, Kentucky	P/hy-me	129
	Malartic, Quebec	R/vs + M/df?	189
	Siegerland, Germany	P/hy	19,148
	Orford Township, Sherbrooke County, Quebec	R/cm	193
	Gap mine, Lancaster County, Pennsylvania	M/df + P/hy	63,148

Species	Locality	Process/type	References
Molybdenite	Climax, Colorado	P/hy-mg	211
	Kingsgate, New South Wales, Australia	P/hy-mg	53
	Aldfield, Quebec	R/sk	199
	Renfrew area, Ontario	R/sk	199
Mottramite	Tsumeb, Namibia	C/ox	215
Narsarsukite	Narssârssuk, Greenland	M/ag	159
	Mont Saint-Hilaire, Quebec	M/ag & R/cm	85,125
Nickeline	Cobalt, Ontario	P/hy	14,78,148
	Port Radium, Northwest Territories	P/hy	197
	Freiberg and Schneeberg, Saxony, Germany	P/hy-mg	121,182
Okenite	Poona, Maharashtra, India	P/hy-bs	40
Orpiment	Hunan Province, China	P/hy	168
	Humboldt County, Nevada	P/hy	191
	Quiruvilca, La Libertad, Peru	P/hy	118
Osumilite	Sardinia, Italy	M/vx	81
	Eifel District, Germany	M/vx	81,83
	Lane County, Oregon	M/vx	81
Pachnolite	Ivigtut, Greenland	C/hp	6,159
Palygorskite	Metalline Falls, Washington	P/hy	22,164
Paravauxite	Llallagua, Bolivia	P/hy	6,8
Pargasite	Pargas, Finland	R/cm	212
Parisite	Muzo, Columbia	P/hy	6,206
	Quincy, Massachusetts	M/gr	149
	Mineral County, Montana	P/hy-mg?	113
Pentlandite	Sudbury, Ontario	M/df	48
	Malartic, Quebec	R/vs	189
Perovskite	Zlatoust, Ural Mtns., Russia	R/cm	5,181
	Magnet Cove, Arkansas	R/cm	148
	Gardiner Complex, Greenland	M/cb	94
	Jacupiranga, São Paulo, Brazil	M/cb	131
	Val Malenco, Lombardy, Italy	R/rd	13,70
	Eifel District, Germany	M/vx	83
Petalite	Minas Gerais, Brazil	M/gr	26
	Oxford County, Maine	M/gr	57,155
	Elba, Italy	M/gr	6,145
Petzite	Nagyag, Romania	P/hy-mg	6,148
	Goldhill, Colorado	P/hy	148,217
Phenakite	Minas Gerais, Brazil	M/gr	23
	Anjanabonoina, Madagascar	M/gr	219
	Chatham, New Hampshire	M/gr	179
	Mount Antero, Colorado	M/gr	86
	Takowaja, Urals, Russia	R/cm	181
	St. Gotthard area, Switzerland	P/al	203
Phillipsite	Melbourne, Victoria, Australia	P/hy-bs	196
	Monument, Oregon	P/hy-bs	196
Phosgenite	Monteponi, Sardinia, Italy	C/ox	5,149
	Cromford, Derbyshire, England	C/ox	20
	Laurium, Greece	C/ox (bi)	105
	Tsumeb, Namibia	C/ox	215
	Tiger, Arizona	C/ox	17
Phospho-phyllite	Potosi, Bolivia	P/hy	5,6
	Hagendorf, Bavaria, Germany	C/hp	135
Phospho-siderite (Metastrengite)	Black Hills, South Dakota	C/hp	135,170
	Pleystein, Bavaria, Germany	C/hp	149
	Indian Mountain, Alabama	P/hy-me	12,67

Species	Locality	Process/type	References
Pollucite	Bernic Lake, Manitoba	M/gr	196
	Oxford County, Maine	M/gr	155,196
	Nuristan, Afghanistan	M/gr	10,196
	Island of Elba, Italy	M/gr	6,145,196
Polybasite	Arizpe, Sonora, Mexico	P/hy	151,202
	Freiberg, Saxony, Germany	P/hy-mg	6,121,182
	Guanajuato, Mexico	P/hy	6,151,202
Powellite	Keewenaw Peninsula, Michigan	P/hy-bs	213
	Nasik, Maharashtra, India	P/hy-bs	110
	Tungsten, Nevada	R/cm	149
	Randsburg, California	C/ox	154
Proustite	Chañarcillo, Atacama, Chile	P/hy-mg	6,34,202
	Freiberg, Saxony, Germany	P/hy-mg	6,121,182
	Pribram & Joachimstal, Bohemia, Czech Republic	P/hy-mg	6,190
	Cobalt, Ontario	P/hy	14,78,148
Pseudo-malachite	Shaba Province, Zaire	C/ox	62
	Libethen, Slovakia	C/ox	149
Pumpellyite	Keewenaw Peninsula, Michigan	P/hy-bs	213
Purpurite	North Groton, New Hampshire	C/hp	41,135,184
Pyrargyrite	Freiberg, Saxony, Germany	P/hy-mg	6,121,182,202
	Andreasberg, Harz, Germany	P/hy-mg	6,121,202
	Fresnillo, Zacatecas, Mexico	P/hy	151,202
	Huancavelica, Peru	P/hy-mg	202,218
	Guanajuato, Mexico	P/hy	5,6,151,202
Pyrrhotite	Santa Eulalia, Chihuahua, Mexico	P/hy	151
	Riondel, British Columbia	P/hy-me?	73
	Nova Lima, Minas Gerais, Brazil	P/hy-mg	124
	Kapnic, Romania	P/hy-mg	6,148
	Trepca, Serbia	P/hy	120
	Sudbury, Ontario	M/df	48
	Malartic, Quebec	R/vs	189
Realgar	Hunan, China	P/hy	168
	Humboldt County, Nevada	P/hy	191
	King County, Washington	P/hy	5,45,164
	Kapnik, Romania	P/hy-mg	6,148
	Binnental, Valais, Switzerland	P/hy-tc	6,69,188
Rhodizite	Antandrokomby, Madagascar	P/gr	205
Roselite	Bou Azzer, Morocco	C/ox	6,150
Samarskite	Iveland, Satersdalen, Norway	M/gr	148,212
	Mitchell County, No. Carolina	M/gr	222
Sapphirine	Fiskenaesset, Greenland	R/rm	158,159
	Betroka, Madagascar	R/rm	42
Scholzite	Hagendorf, Bavaria, Germany	C/hp	135
	Reaphook Hill, South Australia	P/hy-me? + C/ox	95
Schorl	Bovey Tracey, Devon, England	P/hy-mg	52
	Oxford County, Maine	M/gr	56,155
	North Groton, New Hampshire	M/gr	41
	Chester, Vermont	R/rm	71
	Riverside County, California	M/gr	65
Scolecite	Nasik, Maharashtra, India	P/hy-bs	40,196
	Minas Basin, Nova Scotia	P/hy-bs	196
	Rio Grande do Sul, Brazil	P/hy-bs	196
	Cowlitz County, Washington	P/hy-bs	196
Scorodite	Tsumeb, Namibia	C/ox	215
	Concepción del Oro, Zacatecas, Mexico	C/ox	6,151
	Djebel Debar, Constantine, Algeria	C/ox	149
Serendibite	Johnsburg, New York	R/cm	178
Shattuckite	Bisbee, Arizona	C/ox	68

Species	Locality	Process/type	References
Shortite	Green River, Wyoming	P/ev	132
	Mont SaintHilaire, Quebec	R/cm	85,175
Siderite	Nova Lima, Minas Gerais, Brazil	P/hy-mg	124
	Mont Saint-Hilaire, Quebec	M/ag	85,125
	Durham, England	P/mvt	104
	Tavistock, Devon, England	P/hy + C/re	5,52
	Pikes Peak, Colorado	M/gr	55,140
	Allevard, Isère, France	P/al	6
	Rapid Creek, Yukon Territory	P/hy-tc	176
Siegenite	Viburnum Trend, Missouri	P/mvt	116
	Siegen, Westphalia, Germany	P/hy	19,148
Sodalite	Bancroft, Ontario	C/re	84
	Mont Saint-Hilaire, Quebec	M/ag	85,125
Sperrylite	Noril'sk, Siberia, Russia	M/df	46,137
	Sudbury, Ontario	M/df	48
	Transvaal, South Africa	M/df	5
Sphaero-cobaltite (Cobaltocalcite)	Shaba Province, Zaire	P/hy	119
	Concepción del Oro, Zacatecas, Mexico	P/hy	6,151
Stannite	Potosi & Oruro, Bolivia	P/hy	6,8,32
Stephanite	Arizpe, Sonora, Mexico	P/hy	151,202
	Freiberg, Saxony, Germany	P/hy-mg	121,182,202
	Pribram, Bohemia, Czech Republic	P/hy-mg	6,190
Strontianite	Hardin County, Illinois	P/mvt	6,122
	Francon quarry, Montreal, Quebec	M/cb	29
	Strontian, Scotland	P/hy	149
	Winfield, Pennsylvania	P/hy/me	44
	Jamesville, New York	C/bi	44
Sturmanite	Kuruman District, Cape Province, South Africa	P/hy	200
Sugilite	Kuruman District, Cape Province, South Africa	P/hy?	200
Sussexite	Franklin, New Jersey	R/sk	58,59,146
Sylvanite	Cripple Creek, Colorado	P/hy-mg	6,187,217
	Nagyag, Transylvania, Romania	P/hy-mg	6,148
Tantalite	Alto Ligonha, Mozambique	M/gr	6
	Taos County, New Mexico	M/gr	87
	San Diego County, California	M/gr	54
	Gilgit, Pakistan	M/gr	98
Tarbuttite	Broken Hill, Zambia	C/ox	143
	Reaphook Hill, South Australia	C/ox & P/hy	95
Tellurium	Vulcan, Colorado	P/hy	148,169
	Kalgoorlie, Western Australia	P/hy	148
	Moctezuma, Sonora, Mexico	P/hy	60
Tennantite	Tsumeb, Namibia	P/hy	215
	Binnental, Valais, Switzerland	P/hy-tc	6,69,188
	Concepción del Oro, Zacatecas, Mexico (incorrectly ascribed to Naica, Chihuahua)	P/hy	207
Tephroite	Franklin, New Jersey	R/rm	58,59,146
Thenardite	Camp Verde, Arizona	P/ev	195
	Searles Lake, California	P/ev	153,154
Thomsenolite	Ivigtut, Greenland	C/hp	6,159
Thomsonite	Goble, Oregon	P/hy-bs	196
	Renfrewshire, Scotland	P/hy-bs	196
	Asbestos, Quebec	R/rd	77
Thorianite	Fort Dauphin area, Madagascar	R/sk?	5,148
	Otter Lake, Quebec	R/cm	115
	Bancroft area, Ontario	R/cm, M/gr	102

Species	Locality	Process/type	References
Thorite	Bancroft, Ontario	R/cm	102,171
	Eifel District, Germany	M/vx	83
Torbernite	Shaba Province, Zaire	C/ox	6,62
	Mitchell County, North Carolina	C/hp	222
	Gunnislake, Cornwall, England	C/ox	52
Tridymite	Summit Rock, Oregon	M/vx	82
	Thomas Range, Utah	M/vx	82
	Eifel District, Germany	M/vx	83
Trona	Green River, Wyoming	P/ev	132
Tugtupite	Kvanefjeld, Greenland	M/ag + C/hp?	90,159
	Mont Saint-Hilaire, Quebec	M/ag + C/hp?	85
Tyuyamunite	Colorado Plateau area, Utah, Colorado, New Mexico, Arizona	C/ox	78,149
Ulexite	Boron, California	P/ev	3,4,6,139,163
Uraninite	Port Radium, Northwest Territories	P/hy	197
	Joachimstal, Bohemia, Czech Republic	P/hy-mg	6,78
Uranophane	Bancroft, Ontario	C/ox	102,171
	Grants, New Mexico	C/ox	78
	Kolwezi, Shaba, Zaire	C/ox	62
Vauxite	Llallagua, Potosi, Bolivia	P/hy	6,8,218
Veszelyite	Phillipsburg, Montana	C/ox	201
Villiaumite	Isle of Los, Guinea	M/ag	149
	Kvanefjeld, Greenland	M/ag	159
	Mont Saint-Hilaire, Quebec	M/ag	85,125
	Point of Rocks, New Mexico	M/vx	43
Vivianite	Potosi and Oruro, Bolivia	P/hy	6,8,32
	Cobalt, Idaho	P/hy	149,165
	Trepca, Serbia	P/hy	120
Wardite	Taquaral, Minas Gerais, Brazil	C/hp	6,24,135
	Rapid Creek, Yukon Territory	P/hy-tc	176
Wavellite	Llallagua, Potosi, Bolivia	P/hy	8
Whiteite	Rapid Creek, Yukon Territory	P/hy-tc	176
	Custer, South Dakota	C/hp	72
Willemite	Santa Eulalia, Chihuahua, Mexico	C/ox	151
	Tsumeb, Namibia	C/ox	215
	Mont Saint-Hilaire, Quebec	M/ag	85,125
Witherite	Hardin County, Illinois	P/mvt	6,122
	Alston, Cumbria, England	P/mvt?	5,6
	Hexam, Northumberland, England	P/mvt?	44
	Seneca County, New York	C/bi	44
Wurtzite	Llallagua, Potosi, Bolivia	P/hy-mg	6,8
	Butte, Montana	P/hy-mg	6,148
	Thomaston, Connecticut	P/hy-tc?	80
Zinnwaldite	Zinnwald, Bohemia, Czech Republic	P/hy-mg	6
	Pikes Peak, Colorado	M/gr	140
Zoisite	Merelani, Arusha, Tanzania	P/hy-tc+C/r	5,6,11,101
	Ducktown, Tennessee	e	78
	Telemark, Norway	R/vs	212
	Alchuri, Baltistan, Pakistan	R/rm P/hy-tc?	138

Appendix References

1: Adolfsson, Stig G. 1973. "Håkansboda Copper and Cobalt Deposit, Sweden." *Mineralogical Record* 4 (1): 38-39.

2: Appel, Peter, W. Uitterdijk, and Aage Jensen. 1987. "Notes and New Techniques: A New Gem Material from Greenland: Iridescent Orthoamphibole." *Gems & Gemology* Spring: 36-42.

3: Aristarain, L. F., and C. S. Hurlbut, Jr. 1972. "Boron Minerals and Deposits, Part I." *Mineralogical Record* 3 (4): 165-172.

4: Aristarain, L. F., and C. S. Hurlbut, Jr. 1972. "Boron Minerals and Deposits, Part II." *Mineralogical Record* 3 (5): 213-220.

5: Bancroft, Peter. 1973. *The World's Finest Minerals and Crystals.* New York: Viking Press.

6: Bancroft, Peter. 1984. *Gem and Crystal Treasures.* Fallbrook, CA: Western Enterprises.

7: Bancroft, Peter, Joze Car, Mirjan Zorz, and Gregor Kobler. 1991. "Famous Mineral Localities: The Idria Mines, Slovenia, Yugoslavia." *Mineralogical Record* 22 (3): 201-208.

8: Bandy, Mark Chance. 1976. *Mineralogy of Llallagua, Bolivia.* Tucson Gem and Mineral Society Special Paper 1. Tucson.

9: Bariand, P., F. Cesbron, and H. Vachey. 1973. "Hydromagnesite from Soghan, Iran." *Mineralogical Record* 4 (1): 18-21.

10: Bariand, Pierre, and J. F. Poullen. 1978. "Famous Mineral Localities: The Pegmatites of Laghman, Nuristan, Afghanistan." *Mineralogical Record* 9 (5): 301-308.

11: Barot, N. R., and Edward W. Boehm. 1992. "Gem-Quality Green Zoisite." *Gems and Gemology* 28 (1): 4-15.

12: Barwood, Henry. 1974. "Iron Phosphate Mineral Locality at Indian Mountain, Alabama." *Mineralogical Record* 5 (5): 241-244.

13: Bedogné, Francesco, and Renato Pagano. 1972. "Mineral Collecting in Val Malenco." *Mineralogical Record* 3 (3): 120-123.

14: Berry, L. G., ed. 1971. "The Silver-Arsenide Deposits of the Cobalt-Gowganda Region, Ontario. *Canadian Mineralogist* 11 (1): 1-429.

15: Betz, Volker. 1981. "Famous Mineral Localities: Zeolites from Iceland and the Faeroes." *Mineralogical Record* 12 (1): 5-26.

16: Bideaux, Richard A. 1970. "Mineral Rings & Cylinders." *Mineralogical Record* 1 (3): 105-112.

17: Bideaux, Richard A. 1980. "Famous Mineral Localities: Tiger Arizona." *Mineralogical Record* 11 (3): 155-181.

18: Birch, W. D. 1988. "Zeolites from Phillip Island and Flinders, Victoria." *Mineralogical Record* 19 (6): 451-460.

19: Bode, Rainer, and Artur Wittern. 1989. *Mineralien und Fundstellen Bundesrepublik Deutschland.* Haltern: Doris Bode Verlag.

20: Burr, Peter S. 1992. "Notes on the History of Phosgenite and Matlockite from Matlock, England." *Mineralogical Record* 23 (5): 377-386.

21: Cairncross, Bruce. 1991. "The Messina Mining District, South Africa." *Mineralogical Record* 22 (3): 187-199.

22: Cannon, Bart. 1975. *Minerals of Washington.* Mercer Island, WA: Cordilleran Publishing.

23: Cassedanne, J. P. 1985. "Recent Discoveries of Phenakite in Brazil." *Mineralogical Record* 16 (2): 107-109.

24: Cassedanne, Jacques P., and Jeannine O. Cassedanne. 1973. "Minerals from the Lavra da Ilha Pegmatite, Brazil." *Mineralogical Record* 4 (5): 207-213.

25: Cassedanne, Jacques P., and Jeannine O. Cassedanne. 1977. "Axinite, Hydromagnesite, Amethyst and Other Minerals from near Vitória da Conquista (Brazil)." *Mineralogical Record* 8 (5): 382-387.

26: Cassedanne, J., and J. Cassedanne. 1981. "The Urubu Pegmatite and Vicinity." *Mineralogical Record* 12 (2): 73-77.

27: Cassedanne, J. P., and Jack Lowell. 1982. "Famous Mineral Localities: The Virgem da Lapa Pegmatites." *Mineralogical Record* 13 (1): 19-28.

28: Cesbron, F., and P. Bariand. 1975. "The Uranium-Vanadium Deposit of Mounana, Gabon." *Mineralogical Record* 6 (5): 237-249.

29: Chamberlain, Steven C. 1991. "Die Mineralien des Francon-Quarry, Montreal Island, Quebec, Canada." *Mineralien-Welt* June: 59-69.

30: Chamberlain, S. C., and G. W. Robinson. 1993. "Unusual Occurrence of Magnetite Crystals from the Balmat District, St. Lawrence County, New York." *Rocks and Minerals* 68 (3): 122-123 (abstract).

31: Cisneros, S. L., R. E. Witkowski, and D. L. Oswald. 1977. "Artinite from San Benito County, California." *Mineralogical Record* 8 (6): 457-460.

32: Cook, Robert B. 1975. "The Mineralogy of the Department of Oruro, Bolivia." *Mineralogical Record* 6 (3): 125-137.

33: Cook, Robert B. 1978. "Famous Mineral Localities: Chuquicamata, Chile." *Mineralogical Record* 9 (5): 321-333.

34: Cook, Robert B. 1979. "Famous Mineral Localities: Chañarcillo, Chile." *Mineralogical Record* 10 (4): 197-204.

35: Cook, Robert B. 1985. "Famous Mineral Localities: The Mineralogy of Graves Mountain Lincoln County, Georgia." *Mineralogical Record* 16 (6): 443-458.

36: Cooper, M. P., and C. J. Stanley. 1990. *Minerals of the English Lake District.* London: Natural History Museum.

37: Crawford, Jack W. 1988. "Famous Mineral Localities: The Almaden Mines, Cuidad Real, Spain." *Mineralogical Record* 19 (5): 297-302.

38: Crook, Wilson W., III. 1977. "The Clear Creek Pegmatite: A Rare Earth Pegmatite in Brunet County, Texas." *Mineralogical Record* 8 (2): 88-90.

39: Crowley, Jack A. 1977. "Minerals of the Blue Bell Mine, San Bernardino County, California." *Mineralogical Record* 8 (6): 494-496.

40: Currier, Rock H. 1976. "The Production of Zeolite Mineral Specimens from the Deccan Basalt in India." *Mineralogical Record* 7 (5): 248-264.

41: Dallaire, Donald A., and Robert W. Whitmore. 1990. "Mines and Minerals of North Groton, New Hampshire." *Rocks and Minerals* 65 (4): 350-360.

42: Dana, Edward Salisbury, and William E. Ford. 1957. *A Textbook of Mineralogy.* 4th ed. New York: John Wiley & Sons.

43: DeMark, R. S. 1984. "Minerals of Point of Rocks, New Mexico." *Mineralogical Record* 15 (3): 149-156.

44: Dietrich, R. V., and Steven C. Chamberlain. 1989. "Are Cultured Pearls Mineral?" *Rocks and Minerals* 64 (5): 386-392.

45: Dillhoff, Richard M., and Thomas A. Dillhoff. 1991. "Realgar from the Royal Reward Mine, King County, Washington." *Rocks and Minerals* 66 (4): 310-314.

46: Distler, V. V. 1992. "Platinum Mineralization of the Noril'sk Deposits." *Canadian Mineralogist* 30 (2): 480 (abstract).

47: Donnay, Gabrielle, C. O. Ingamells, and Brian Mason. 1966. "Buergerite, a New Species of Tourmaline." *American Mineralogist* 51 (1): 198-199.

48: Dressler, B. O., V. K. Supta, and T. L. Muir. 1991. "The Sudbury Structure." In *Geology of Ontario,* Edited by P.C. Thurston, H.R. Williams, R.H. Sutcliffe and G.M. Scott, Ontario Geological Survey Special Vol. 4, 593-625. Ministry of Northern Development and Mines, Toronto.

49: Dunn, Pete J., Peter B. Leavens, and Cynthia Barnes. 1980. "Magnesioaxinite from Luning, Nevada, and Some Nomenclature Designations for the Axinite Group." *Mineralogical Record* 11 (1): 13-15.

50: Dunn, Pete J., Peter B. Leavens, B. Darko Sturman, Richard V. Gaines, and Carlos do Prado Barbosa. 1979. "Hureaulite and Barbosalite from Lavra do Criminoso, Minas Gerais, Brazil." *Mineralogical Record* 10 (3):147-151.

51: Dunning, G. E., and J. F. Cooper, Jr. 1987. "Inesite from the Hale Creek Mine, Trinity County, California." *Mineralogical Record* 18 (5): 341-347.

52: Embrey, P. G., and R. F. Symes. 1987. *Minerals of Cornwall and Devon.* London: British Museum (Natural History).

53: England, Brian M. 1985. "Famous Mineral Localities: The Kingsgate Mines, New South Wales, Australia." *Mineralogical Record* 16 (4): 265-289.

54: Foord, Eugene E. 1977. "The Himalaya Dike System: Mesa Grande District, San Diego County, California." *Mineralogical Record* 8 (6): 461-474.

55: Foord, Eugene E., and Robert F. Martin. 1979. "Amazonite from the Pikes Peak Batholith." *Mineralogical Record* 10 (6): 375-376.

56: Francis, Carl A. 1985. "Maine Tourmaline." *Mineralogical Record* 16 (5): 365-388.

57: Francis, Carl A. 1987. "Minerals of the Topsham, Maine, Pegmatite District." *Rocks and Minerals* 62 (6): 407-415.

58: Frondel, Clifford. 1972. *The Minerals of Franklin and Sterling Hill: A Check List.* New York: Wiley-Interscience.

59: Frondel, Clifford, and John L. Baum. 1974. "Structure and Mineralogy of the Franklin Zinc-Iron-Manganese Deposit, New Jersey." *Economic Geology* 69 (2): 157-180.

60: Gaines, Richard V. 1970. "The Moctezuma Tellurium Deposit." *Mineralogical Record* 1 (2): 40-43.

61: Gauthier, Gilbert, and Nicolaos Albandakis. 1991. "Minerals of the Seriphos Skarn, Greece." *Mineralogical Record* 22 (4): 303-308.

62: Gauthier, Gilbert, Armand François, M. Deliens, and P. Piret. 1989. "Famous Mineral Localities: The Uranium Deposits of the Shaba Region, Zaire." *Mineralogical Record* 20 (4): 265-288.

63: Geyer, Alan R., Robert C. Smith, II, and John H. Barnes. 1976. *Mineral Collecting in Pennsylvania.* 4th ed. Pennsylvania Geological Survey General Geology Report 33. Commonwealth of Pennsylvania Department of Environmental Resources Topographic and Geologic Survey, Harrisburg.

64: Gillanders, R. J. 1981. "Famous Mineral Localities: The Leadhills-Wanlockhead District, Scotland." *Mineralogical Record* 12 (4): 235-250.

65: Gochenour, Kenneth. 1988. "Black Tourmaline from Little Cahuilla Mountain, Riverside County, California." *Rocks and Minerals* 63 (6): 440-444.

66: Goldblum, Deborah R., and Mary Louise Hill. 1992. "Enhanced Fluid Flow Resulting from Competency Contrast within a Shear Zone: The Garnet Ore Zone at Gore Mountain, NY." *Journal of Geology* 100: 776-782.

67: Gordon, Jennings B., Jr., and Curtis L. Hollabaugh. 1989. "Phosphate Microminerals of the Indian Mountain Area." *Mineralogical Record* 20 (5): 355-362.

68: Graeme, Richard W. 1981. "Famous Mineral Localities: Bisbee, Arizona." *Mineralogical Record* 12 (5): 258-319.

69: Graeser, Stefan. 1977. "Famous Mineral Localities: Lengenbach, Switzerland." *Mineralogical Record* 8 (4): 275-281.

70: Gramaccioli, Carlo M. 1979. "Minerals of the Alpine Rodingites of Italy." *Mineralogical Record* 10 (2): 85-89.

71: Grant, Raymond W. 1968. *Mineral Collecting in Vermont.* Vermont Geological Survey Special Publication No. 2. Vermont Geological Survey, Montpellier.

72: Grice, Joel D., Pete J. Dunn, and Robert A. Ramik. 1989. "Whiteite-(CaMnMg), a New Mineral from the Tip Top Pegmatite, Custer, South Dakota." *Canadian Mineralogist* 27: 699-702.

73: Grice, J. D., and R. A. Gault. 1977. "The Bluebell Mine, Riondel, British Columbia, Canada." *Mineralogical Record* 8 (1): 33-36.

74: Grice, J. D., and R. A. Gault. 1981. "Edingtonite and Natrolite from Ice River, British Columbia." *Mineralogical Record* 12 (4): 221-226.

75: Grice, J. D., and R. A. Gault. 1983. "Lapis Lazuli from Lake Harbour, Baffin Island, Canada." *Rocks and Minerals* 58 (1): 12-19.

76: Grice, J. D., Robert A. Gault, and H. Gary Ansell. 1984. "Edingtonite: The First Two Canadian Occurrences." *Canadian Mineralogist* 22 (2): 253-258.

77: Grice, J. D., and R. Williams. 1979. "The Jeffrey Mine, Asbestos, Quebec." *Mineralogical Record* 10 (2): 69-80.

78: Guilbert, John M., and Charles F. Park, Jr. 1986. *The Geology of Ore Deposits.* New York: W. H. Freeman.

79: Gutzmer, Jens, and Bruce Cairncross. 1993. "Recent Discoveries from the Wessels Mine, South Africa." *Mineralogical Record* 24 (5): 365-368.

80: Henderson, William A., Jr. 1979. "Microminerals." *Mineralogical Record* 10 (4): 239-241.

81: Henderson, William A., Jr. 1981. "Microminerals." *Mineralogical Record* 12 (6): 381-385.

82: Henderson, William A., Jr. 1985. "Microminerals of the Western Volcanics." *Mineralogical Record* 16 (2): 137-135.

83: Hentschel, Gerhard. 1983. *Die Mineralien der Eifelvulkane.* Munich: Christian Weise Verlag.

84: Hewitt, D. F. 1961. *Nepheline Syenite Deposits of Southern Ontario.* Toronto: Ontario Department of Mines.

85: Horvath, Laszlo, and Robert A. Gault. 1990. "The Mineralogy of Mont Saint-Hilaire Quebec." *Mineralogical Record* 21 (4): 284-359.

86: Jacobson, Mark I. 1979. "Famous Mineral Localities: Mount Antero." *Mineralogical Record* 10 (6): 339-346.

87: Jahns, Richard H., and Rodney C. Ewing. 1977. "The Harding Mine, Taos County, New Mexico." *Mineralogical Record* 8 (2): 115-126.

88: Januzzi, Ronald E. 1966. *A Field Mineralogy of the Tilly Foster Iron Mine at Tilly Foster, Brewster, New York.* Brewster, NY: The Mineralogical Press.

89: Jaszczak, John A. 1991. "Graphite from Crestmore, California." *Mineralogical Record* 22 (6): 427-432.

90: Jensen, Aage, and Ole V. Petersen. 1982. "Tugtupite: A Gemstone from Greenland." *Gems & Gemology* 28: 90-94.

91: Jensen, David E. 1978. *Minerals of New York State.* Rochester, NY: Ward Press.

92: Jensen, Martin. 1985. "The Majuba Hill Mine: Pershing County." *Mineralogical Record* 16 (1): 57-72.

93: Jensen, Martin. 1993. "Update on the Mineralogy of the Majuba Hill Mine, Pershing County, Nevada." *Mineralogical Record* 24 (3): 171-180.

94: Johnsen, Ole, Ole Petersen, and Olaf Medenbach. 1985. "The Gardiner Complex, a New Locality in Greenland." *Mineralogical Record* 16 (6): 485-494.

95: Johnston, Christopher W., and Roderick J. Hill. 1978. "Zinc Phosphates at Reaphook Hill, South Australia." *Mineralogical Record* 9 (1): 20-25.

96: Jones, Robert W. 1980. "The Grand Reef Mine, Graham County, Arizona." *Mineralogical Record* 11 (4): 219-225.

97: Joyce, D. K., R. I. Gait, and B. D. Sturman. 1994. "The Morphology, Physical Properties and Occurrence of Howlite from Iona, Nova Scotia." *Rocks and Minerals* 69 (2): 119 (abstract).

98: Kazmi, Ali H., Joseph J. Peters, and Herbert P. Obodda. 1985. "Gem Pegmatites of the Shingus-Dusso Area: Gilgit, Pakistan." *Mineralogical Record* 16 (5): 393-412.

99: Kearns, Lance E. 1978. "The Amity Area, Orange County, New York." *Mineralogical Record* 9 (2): 85-90.

100: Keller, Peter C. 1990. *Gemstones and Their Origins.* New York: Van Nostrand Reinhold.

101: Keller, Peter C. 1992. *Gemstones of East Africa.* Phoenix: Geoscience Press.

102: Kennedy, Irwin. 1979. "Some Interesting Radioactive Minerals from the Bancroft Area, Ontario." *Mineralogical Record* 10 (3): 153-158.

103: Kidwell, Albert L. 1989. "Phosphate Minerals of Arkansas." *Rocks and Minerals* 64 (5): 189-195.

104: King, Robert J. 1982. "The Boltsburn Mine, Weardale, County Durham, England." *Mineralogical Record* 13 (1): 5-18.

105: Kohlberger, William. 1976. "Minerals of the Laurium Mines: Attica, Greece." *Mineralogical Record* 7 (3): 114-125.

106: Kokinos, Michael, and William S. Wise. 1993. "Famous Mineral Localities: The Gold Hill Mine, Tooele County, Utah." *Mineralogical Record* 24 (1): 11-22.

107: Kolesar, Peter. 1990. "Dyskrasit-Kristalle aus dem Bergbau-Revier Pribram in der Tschechoslowakei." *Lapis* 15 (9): 19-26.

108: Korowski, Stanley P., and Cor W. Notebaart. 1978. "Libethenite from the Rokana Mine, Zambia." *Mineralogical Record* 9 (6): 341-346.

109: Kosnar, Richard A., and Harold W. Miller. 1976. "Crystallized Minerals of the Colorado Mineral Belt." *Mineralogical Record* 7 (6): 278-307.

110: Kothavala, Rustam Z. 1982. "The Discovery of Powellite at Nasik, India." *Mineralogical Record* 13 (5): 303-309.

111: Kothavala, Rustam Z. 1991. "The Wagholi Cavansite Locality near Poona, India." *Mineralogical Record* 22 (6): 415-420.

112: Larson, Bill. 1977. "The Best of San Diego County." *Mineralogical Record* 8 (6): 507-518.

113: Lasmanis, R. 1977. "The Snowbird Mine, Montana's Parisite Locality." *Mineralogical Record* 8 (2): 83-86.

114: Lauf, Robert J. 1983. "Graphite from the Lead Hill Mine, Ticonderoga, New York." *Mineralogical Record* 14 (1): 25-30.

115: Leavitt, D. 1981. "Minerals of the Yates Uranium Mine, Pontiac County, Quebec." *Mineralogical Record* 12 (6): 359-363.

116: Le Font, Mark. 1984. "Siegenite from the Buick Mine, Bixby, Missouri." *Mineralogical Record* 15 (1): 3739.

117: Leicht, Wayne C. 1971. "Minerals of the Grandview Mine." *Mineralogical Record* 2 (5): 214-221.

118: Lewis, Richard W., Jr. 1956. "The Geology and Ore Deposits of the Quiruvilca District, Peru." *Economic Geology* 51: 41-63.

119: Lhoest, Joseph J., Gilbert Gauthier, and Vandall T. King. 1991. "Famous Mineral Localities: The Mashamba West Mine, Shaba, Zaire." *Mineralogical Record* 22 (1): 13-20.

120: Lieber, Werner. 1973. "Trepca and Its Minerals." *Mineralogical Record* 4 (2): 56-61.

121: Lieber, Werner, and Hermann Leyerzapf. 1986. "German Silver: An Historical Perspective on Silver Mining in Germany." *Mineralogical Record* 17 (1): 3-18.

122: Lillie, Ross C. 1988. "Minerals of the Harris Creek Fluorspar District, Hardin County, Illinois." *Rocks and Minerals* 63 (3): 210-226.

123: Lincks, G. Fred. 1978. "The Chester Emery Mines." *Mineralogical Record* 9 (4): 235-242.

124: Lucio, A., and Richard V. Gaines. 1973. "The Minerals of the Morro Velho Gold Mine, Brazil." *Mineralogical Record* 4 (5): 224-229.

125: Mandarino, J. A., and V. Anderson. 1989. *Monteregian Treasures: The Minerals of Mont Saint-Hilaire, Quebec.* Cambridge: Cambridge University Press.

126: Marty, Joe, Martin C. Jensen, and Andrew D. Roberts. 1993. "Minerals of the Centennial Eureka Mine, Tintic District, Eureka, Utah." *Rocks and Minerals* 68 (6): 406-416.

127: Mason, Brian. 1976. "Famous Mineral Localities: Broken Hill, Australia." *Mineralogical Record* 7 (1): 25-33.

128: McColl, Don, and Gladys Warren. 1984. "Kornerupine and Sapphirine Crystals from the Harts Range, Central Australia." *Mineralogical Record* 15 (2): 99-101.

129: Medici, John C. 1981. "The Halls Gap Millerite Locality." *Rocks and Minerals* 56 (3): 104-108.

130: Melanson, Frank, and George Robinson. 1982. "The Fluorite Mines of Madoc, Ontario." *Mineralogical Record* 13 (2): 87-92.

131: Menezes, Luiz Alberto Dias, and Joaniel Munhoz Martins. 1984. "The Jacupiranga Mine, São Paulo, Brazil." *Mineralogical Record* 15 (5): 261-270.

132: Milton, Charles. 1977. "Mineralogy of the Green River Formation." *Mineralogical Record* 8 (5): 368-379.

133: Mitchell, Richard S. 1977. "Some Noteworthy Minerals from Virginia." *Rocks and Minerals* 52 (5): 221-229.

134: Moore, Paul B. 1970. "Mineralogy & Chemistry of Långban-Type Deposits in Bergslagen, Sweden." *Mineralogical Record* 1 (4): 154-172.

135: Moore, Paul Brian. 1973. "Pegmatite Phosphates: Descriptive Mineralogy and Crystal Chemistry." *Mineralogical Record* 4 (3): 103-130.

136: Moore, Thomas P. 1987. "Notes from Germany." *Mineralogical Record* 18 (2): 159-163.

137: Moore, Thomas. 1992. "What's New in Minerals: Tucson Show." *Mineralogical Record* 23 (3): 273-281.

138: Moore, Thomas. 1993. "What's New in Minerals: Tucson Show." *Mineralogical Record* 24 (3): 219-230, 237.

139: Muessig, Siegfried. 1959. "Primary Borates in Playa Deposits: Minerals of High Hydration." *Economic Geology* 54: 495-501.

140: Muntyan, Barbara L., and John R. Muntyan. 1985. "Minerals of the Pikes Peak Granite." *Mineralogical Record* 16 (3): 217-230.

141: Murphy, Jack A. 1979. "The San Juan Mountains of Colorado." *Mineralogical Record* 10 (6): 349-361.

142: Niedermayr, Gerhard. 1986. "Mineral Localities in Austria." *Mineralogical Record* 17 (2): 105-110.

143: Notebaart, C. W., and S. P. Korowski. 1980. "Famous Mineral Localities: The Broken Hill Mine, Zambia." *Mineralogical Record* 11 (6): 339-348.

144: Novak, G. A., and S. G. Oswald. 1971. "Laumontite from the Pine Creek Mine, Bishop, California." *Mineralogical Record* 2 (5): 222.

145: Orlandi, Paolo, and Pier Bruno Scortecci. 1985. "Minerals of the Elba Pegmatites." *Mineralogical Record* 16 (5): 353-363.

146: Palache, Charles. 1935. *The Minerals of Franklin and Sterling Hill, Sussex County, New Jersey.* United States Geological Survey Professional Paper 180. United States Department of the Interior, Washington.

147: Palache, Charles. 1936. "Babingtonite and Epidote from Westfield, Massachusetts." *American Mineralogist* 21: 652-655.

148: Palache, Charles, Harry Berman, and Clifford Frondel. 1944. *The System of Mineralogy of James Dwight Dana and Edward Salisbury Dana, Yale University 1837-1892.* 7th ed. Vol. 1. New York: John Wiley and Sons.

149: Palache, Charles, Harry Berman, and Clifford Frondel. 1951. *The System of Mineralogy of James Dwight Dana and Edward Salisbury Dana, Yale University 1837-1892.* 7th ed. Vol. 2. New York: John Wiley and Sons.

150: Pallix, Gerard. 1978. "Famous Mineral Localities: Bou-Azzer, Morocco." *Mineralogical Record* 9 (2): 69-73.

151: Panczner, William D. 1987. *Minerals of Mexico.* New York: Van Nostrand Reinhold.

152: Pearl, Richard M. 1974. "Minerals of the Pikes Peak Granite." *Mineralogical Record* 5 (4): 183-189.

153: Pemberton, Earl H. 1975. "The Crystal Habits and Forms of the Minerals of Searles Lake, San Bernardino County, California." *Mineralogical Record* 6 (2): 74-83.

154: Pemberton, Earl H. 1983. *Minerals of California.* New York: Van Nostrand Reinhold.

155: Perham, Jane C. 1987. *Maine's Treasure Chest: Gems and Minerals of Oxford County.* West Paris, ME: Quicksilver Publications.

156: Peters, Joseph J. 1984. "Triassic Traprock Minerals of New Jersey." *Rocks and Minerals* 59 (4): 157-183.

157: Peters, Thomas A., Joseph J. Peters, and Julius Weber. 1978. "Famous Mineral Localities: Paterson, New Jersey." *Mineralogical Record* 9 (3): 157-179.

158: Petersen, Ole V., Ole Johnsen, and Aage Jensen. 1980. "Giant Crystals of Kornerupine." *Mineralogical Record* 11 (2): 93-96.

159: Petersen, Ole V., and Karsten Secher. 1993. "The Minerals of Greenland." *Mineralogical Record* 24 (2): 4-67.

160: Pohl, Demetrius, Renald Guillemette, and James Shigley. 1982. "Ferroaxinite from New Melones Lake, Calaveras County, California, a Remarkable New Locality." *Mineralogical Record* 13 (5): 293-302.

161: Prenn, Neil, and Peggy Merrick. 1991. "The Monitor-Mogul Mining District, Alpine County, California." *Mineralogical Record* 22 (1): 29-40.

162: Pring, Allan. 1988. "Minerals of the Moonta and Wallaroo Mining Districts, South Australia." *Mineralogical Record* 19 (6): 407-416.

163: Puffer, J. H. 1975. "The Kramer Borate Mineral Assemblage, Boron, California." *Mineralogical Record* 6 (2): 84-91.

164: Ream, Lanny R. 1985. *Gems and Minerals of Washington.* Renton, WA: Jackson Mountain Press.

165: Ream, Lanny R. 1989. *Idaho Minerals.* Coeur d'Alene, ID: L. R. Ream Publishing.

166: Ream, Lanny R. 1991. "Two Autunite Localities in Northeastern Washington, The Daybreak and Triple H & J Mines." *Rocks and Minerals* 66 (4): 294-297.

167: Reasenberg, Julian. 1968. "New Artinite Find on Staten Island, New York." *Rocks and Minerals* 43 (9): 643-647.

168: Ren, Kai-Wen. 1980. *Minerals in China.* Shanghai, China: Shanghai Scientific and Technical Publishers.

169: Rickard. T. A.; annotated by Arthur E. Smith and Richard A. Kosnar. 1983. "Across the San Juan Mountains." *Mineralogical Record* 14 (4): 243-249.

170: Roberts, Willard Lincoln, and George Rapp, Jr. 1965. *Mineralogy of the Black Hills.* South Dakota School of Mines and Technology, Bulletin No. 18. Rapid City, SD.

171: Robinson, George, and Steven C. Chamberlain. 1982. "An Introduction to the Mineralogy of Ontario's Grenville Province." *Mineralogical Record* 13 (2): 71-86.

172: Robinson, George W., and Joel D. Grice. 1993. "The Barium Analog of Brewsterite from Harrisville, New York." *Canadian Mineralogist* 31 (3): 687-690.

173: Robinson, George W., and Vandall T. King. 1990. "What's New in Minerals?" *Mineralogical Record* 21 (5): 481-492, 501.

174: Robinson, George W., and Vandall T. King. 1993. "What's New in Minerals?" *Mineralogical Record* 24 (5): 381394.

175: Robinson, George W., Vandall T. King, Eric Asselborn, Forrest Cureton, Rudy Tschernich, and Robert Sielecki. 1992. "What's New in Minerals?" *Mineralogical Record* 23 (5): 423-437.

176: Robinson, George W., Jerry Van Velthuizen, H. Gary Ansell, and B. Darko Sturman. 1992. "Mineralogy of the Rapid Creek and Big Fish River Area, Yukon Territory." *Mineralogical Record* 23 (4): 4-47.

177: Rossman, George R., and Richard L. Squires. 1974. "The Occurrence of Alstonite at Cave in Rock, Illinois." *Mineralogical Record* 5 (6): 266-269.

178: Rowley, Elmer B. 1987. "Serendibite, Sinhalite, Sapphirine, and Grandidierite from the Adirondack Mountains, at Johnsburg, New York." *Rocks and Minerals* 62 (4): 243-246.

179: Samuelson, Peter B., Kenneth H. Hollmann, and Carlton L. Holt. 1990. "Minerals of the Conway and Mount Osceola Granites of New Hampshire." *Rocks and Minerals* 65 (4): 286-296.

180: Sansoni, Gerhard. 1993. "Über Akanthit, insbesondere aus dem Freiberger Revier." *Mineralien-Welt* 4 (2): 36-40.

181: Scalisi, Philip, and David Cook. 1983. *Classic Mineral Localities of the World: Asia and Australia.* New York: Van Nostrand Reinhold.

182: Schröder, Boris, and Ulrich Lipp. 1990. "Der Uranerzbergbau der SDAG-Wismut im Roum Schneeberg-Aue-Schlema und seine Mineralien (II)." *Mineralien-Welt* Heft 3 (November-December): 20-44.

183: Seemann, Robert. 1986. "Famous Mineral Localities: Knappenwand, Untersulzbachtal, Austria." *Mineralogical Record* 17 (3): 167-181.

184: Segeler, Curt G., Anthony R. Kampf, William Ulrich, and Robert W. Whitmore. 1981. "Phosphate Minerals of the Palermo No.1 Pegmatite." *Rocks and Minerals* 56 (5): 197-214.

185: Skobel', L. S., I. I. Nekhanenko, and N. P. Popova. 1993. "Axinitfunde in der Lagerstätte Puiva, Polarural." *Mineralien-Welt* 4 (5): 33-37.

186: Smith, Arthur E. 1991. "Texas Mineral Locality Index." *Rocks and Minerals* 66 (3): 196-224.

187: Smith, Arthur E., Jr., Ed Raines, and Leland Feitz. 1985. "Great Pockets: The Cresson Vug, Cripple Creek." *Mineralogical Record* 16 (3): 231-238.

188: Stalder, H. A., P. Embrey, S. Graeser, and W. Nowacki. 1978. *Die Mineralien des Binntales.* Bern: Naturhistorisches Museum der Stadt Bern.

189: Staveley, R. C. 1976. "Minerals of Marbridge Mines Limited." *Mineralogical Record* 7 (4): 174-178.

190: Stobbe, J. 1981. "Famous Mineral Localities: Príbram, Czechoslovakia." *Mineralogical Record* 12 (3): 157-165.

191: Stolburg, Craig S., and Gail E. Dunning. 1985. "The Getchell Mine, Humboldt County, Nevada." *Mineralogical Record* 16 (1): 15-23.

192: Taggard, Joseph E., Abraham Rosenzweig, and Eugene E. Foord. 1989. "Famous Mineral Localities: The Hansonburg District, Bingham, New Mexico." *Mineralogical Record* 20 (1): 31-46.

193: Tarassoff, P. 1993. "History and Mineralogy of the Orford Nickel Mine, Orford Township, Quebec." In *Proceedings of the 20th Annual Mineralogical Symposium,* 27 (abstract). Rochester, NY: Rochester Academy of Science.

194: Thomas, William J., and Ronal B. Gibbs. 1983. "Famous Mineral Localities: The New Cornelia Mine, Ajo, Arizona." *Mineralogical Record* 14 (5): 283-298.

195: Thompson, Robert J. 1983. "Camp Verde Evaporites." *Mineralogical Record* 14 (2): 85-96.

196: Tschernich, Rudy W. 1992. *Zeolites of the World.* Phoenix: Geoscience Press.

197: Tyson, Rod. 1989. "The Port Radium District, Northwest Territories, Canada." *Mineralogical Record* 20 (3): 201-208.

198: Van Velthuizen, Jerry. 1993. "The Parker Mine, Notre Dame du Laus, Quebec." *Mineralogical Record* 24 (5): 369-373.

199: Vokes, F. M. 1963. *Molybdenum Deposits of Canada.* Geological Survey of Canada Economic Geology Report No. 20. Geological Survey of Canada, Ottawa.

200: Von Bezing, K. L., Roger D. Dixon, Demetrius Pohl, and Greg Cavallo. 1991. "The Kalahari Manganese Field: An Update." *Mineralogical Record* 22 (4): 279-297.

201: Waisman, Dave. 1992. "Minerals of the Black Pine Mine, Granite County, Montana." *Mineralogical Record* 23 (6): 477-483.

202: Wallace, Terry C., Mark Barton, and Wendell E. Wilson. 1994. "Silver and Silver-bearing Minerals." *Rocks and Minerals* 69 (1): 16-38.

203: Weibel, M. 1966. *A Guide to the Minerals of Switzerland.* New York: Interscience, Wiley.

204: Weiner, K. L., and Rupert Hochleitner. 1987. "Steckbrief: Ilvait." *Lapis* 12 (4): 7-9.

205: Weiner, K. L., and Rupert Hochleitner. 1990. "Steckbrief: Rhodizit." *Lapis* 15 (2): 7-9.

206: White, John S. 1971. "What's New in Minerals." *Mineralogical Record* 2 (5): 231.

207: White, John S. 1972. "Tennantite-Tetrahedrite from Naica, Chihuahua, Mexico." *Mineralogical Record* 3 (3): 115-119.

208: White, John S. 1974. "Mineral Notes: New Minerals." *Mineralogical Record* 5 (2): 74.

209: White, John S. 1975. "What's New in Minerals?" *Mineralogical Record* 6 (1): 38-40.

210: White, John S., and J. A. Nelen. 1985. "Hutchinsonite from Quiruvilca, Peru." *Mineralogical Record* 16 (6): 459-460.

211: White, W. H., A. A. Bookstrom, R. J. Kamilli, M. W. Ganster, R. P. Smith, D. E. Ranta, and R. C. Steininger. 1981. "Character and Origin of Climax-Type Molybdenum Deposits." *Economic Geology* 75th Anniversary Vol.: 270-316.

212: Wilke, Hans-Jürgen. 1976. *Mineral-Fundstellen.* Vol. 4, Skandinavien. Munich: Christian Weise Verlag.

213: Wilson, Marc L., and Stanley J. Dyl, II. 1992. "The Michigan Copper Country." *Mineralogical Record* 23 (2): 4-72.

214: Wilson, W. E. 1976. "Famous Mineral Localities: Saint John's Island, Egypt." *Mineralogical Record* 7 (6): 310-314.

215: Wilson, Wendell E., ed. 1977. "Tsumeb! The World's Greatest Mineral Locality." *Mineralogical Record* 8 (3): 1-128.

216: Wilson, W. E. 1981. "What's New in Minerals?" *Mineralogical Record* 12 (3): 177-186.

217: Wilson, W. E. 1982. "The Gold-containing Minerals: A Review." *Mineralogical Record* 13 (6): 389-400.

218: Wilson, W. E. 1982. "What's New in Minerals?" *Mineralogical Record* 13 (1): 39-42.

219: Wilson, Wendell E. 1989. "The Anjanabonoina Pegmatite, Madagascar." *Mineralogical Record* 20 (3): 191-200.

220: Wilson, W. E., and Pete J. Dunn. 1978. "Famous Mineral Localities: The Kalahari Manganese Field." *Mineralogical Record* 9 (3): 137-153.

221: Wilson, W. E., and J. S. White. 1976. "What's New in Minerals?" *Mineralogical Record* 7 (2): 55-59.

222: Wilson, W. F., and B. J. McKenzie. 1978. *Mineral Collecting Sites in North Carolina.* Information Circular 24. Raleigh, NC: North Carolina Geological Survey.

223: Wise, William S. 1977. "Mineralogy of the Champion Mine, White Mountains, California." *Mineralogical Record* 8 (6): 478-486.

224: Worner, H. K., and R. W. Mitchell, eds. 1982. *Minerals of Broken Hill.* Melbourne: Australia Mining & Smelting.

225: Zebec, Vladimir, and Marin Soufek. 1986. "Hyalophan von Busovaca, Jugoslawien." *Lapis* 11 (1): 28-31.

Index

Acanthite 105
Acid 69, 110, 111, 117, 149
Acid rain 111
Actinolite 162, 171
Adamite 124
Aegirine 56, **57**, 179
Agate 24, **82**, 84, 85
Agpaite 56–60
Agricola, Georgius 75
Albite 42, 49, **50**, **51**, 57, **59**, 185
Alexandrite 166
Almandine **48**, **158**, 159, 179
Alpine cleft 95, 97, 175
Aluminum 16, 31, 52, 55, 56, 72, 73, 85,
   99, 111, 137, 141, 156, 157, 159, 160,
   162, 167, 171, 181, 191, 195
Amazonite **50**
Amblygonite 55, 137
Amethyst 55, 82, **83**, 85
Amphiboles 33, 39, 56, 154, 166, 171
Amphilobolite 166
Analcime **58**, 59, 85
Anapaite **190**, 191
Anatase 95
Andadite 177
Andalusite 21, 155, 156, 157
Andesite 31
Andradite 171
Anglesite **122**, 123
Anhydrite 109, 191
Anions 65, 100, 101, 105–106, 110, 117,
   123, 124, 136, 148, 149
Antimony 89, 91, 123, 132, 135, **136**, 147
Apatite 39
Apophyllite **20**, 85
Aquamarine 46, 49
Aqueous solutions 22, 24, 25, 27, 65, 69, 70,
   73, 74, 75, 82, 85, 88, 91, 100, 110, 124,
   130, 148, 154, 193, 194
Aragonite 24, 25, 70, 73, 192
Arfvedsonite 56
Arkansas, Quachita Mountains (Hot Springs)
   93, 94
Arsenic 88, 89, 92, 99, 123, 124
Asphalt 79, 81
Assimulation 34 (FIGURE D), 35, 60
Aureole 165, 171, 180
Aurichalcite 124, **125**
Austria, Swiss Alps—Utersulzbachtal 99
Autunite 109
Azurite **22**, 25, 119, **120**, 123
Barite **70**, 73, **80**, 81, 147
Barium 33, 56, 99
Barrow George 159
Basalt 16, 20, 31, 32, 33, 38, 39, **82**, 84, 85,
   186
Bases 110
Basin 67, 68, 77
Bauxite 111

Bedrock 111
Benitoite **98**, 99
Beryl 25, **44**, 45, **46**, 137, **164**, 165, 166,
   184, 185. *See also* Emerald
Beryllium 34, 35, 42, 45, 56, 137, 141, 165,
   186
Betrandite 137
Biogenic origin 189, 192
Biotite 55, 171
Bixbyite 45
Black smokers 10, 186
Borates 67, 68
Borax 67, 100, 108, 109
Bornite **88**, 89
Boron 34, 45, 49, 61, 68, 137, 166
Botryoid 73
Bournonite 89
Bowen, Norman 32, 34
Brazil, Minas Gerais 38, 42, 46, 50, 52, 139
Breccia 87, **119**
Brine 60, 77, 79, 81, 100, 186
Bromine 60
Brookite 95
Brushite 191
Calcite **18**, 19, 21, **22**, 24, 25, **40**, 57, **68**, 69,
   70, 73, **76**, 77, 79, **80**, 81, **104**, 105, 111,
   114, 141, **142**, 143, 157, 159, 162, **163**,
   167, **169**, 172, **173**, 185
Calcium 16, 24, 25, 32, 33, 69, 81, 85, 95,
   99, 109, 111, 143, 157, 159, 171, 181,
   189, 191
Carbon 38, 41, 69, 71, 73
Carbonate 35, 38, 39, 40, 41, 57, 59, 69, 73,
   77, 81, 123, 124, 159, 194
Carbonatite 21, 35, 39–42, 56
Cassiterite 55, **86**, 92, 167
Catapleiite 60
Cations 65, 100, 105, 113, 117, 123, 124,
   137, 148, 149
Cerium 54
Cerussite **123**
Chalcanthite **133**
Chalcocite 89
Chalcopyrite **22**, 25, **76**, 77, 79, **88**, 89, 92,
   123, 167, 186
Charoite **178**, 179
Chemical alteration of preexisting
   minerals 24, 25–27, 105, 106
Chemosynthesis 189
Childrenite 141
Chloride 65, 77, 80, 81, 100
Chlorine 60, 87
Chlorite 95, 141, 155, 159
Chromian Diopside **38**
Chromite 35
Chromium 25, 38, 46, 49, 99, 166, 177
Chromophores 49
Chrysoberyl **46**, 49, 166
Chrysocolla 87, 119, 120, 124

Chrysotile asbestos 162
Clay 23, 73, 77, 85, 111, 157, 159
Cleopatra, Queen 166
Clinochlore **99**, 175, **178**
Clinozoisite 177
Cobalt 88, 92, 132
Cobaltite 132
Coesite 195
Colemanite 67, **68**
Collinsite 95
Colombia, Muzo and Chivor Districts 184,
   185, 186
Columbite 42
Compaction 24
Compounds 18, 19, 67, 81
Convection 14–16
Cookeite 137
Copper 22, 24, 49, 75, 77, **84**, 88, 89, 92,
   100, **118**, 119, 120, 123, 124, 184, **192**
Cordierite 141, **158**, 159
Corundum 160, **161**, 162
Crandallite 72
Cristobalite **82**, 195
Crocoite **128**, 132
Crust 13, 14, 15, 16, 17, 31, 38, 43, 49, 74,
   75
Crystal 11, 18, 19, 20, 21, 22, 30, 31, 32,
   33, 40, 41, 43, 44, 45, 46, 48, 49, 50–55,
   57, 59, 60, 61, 65, 67, 71, 75, 79, 80–81,
   84, 85, 87
Crystallization 20, 21, 23, 31, 32,
   33 (FIGURE C), 35, 37, 41, 43, 45, 54, 56,
   57, 59, 60, 61, 65, 67, 75, 82, 84, 85, 137
   from molten rock 24, 25, 27, 30–61
   recrystallization by heat and pressure 24,
   25, 27, 75. *See also* Recrystallization
Cubanite **184**
Cuprite **118**, 119, **120**, **192**
Cuprosklodowskite **131**
Datolite 85
Dendrites **70**, 73
Diamond 19, 21, 25, **36**, 37, **38**, 185
Differentiation 34, 35, 40, 41, 42, 56, 60,
   61, 75, 87, 89
Diffusion 34 (FIGURE D), 35, 61, 165
Dike 34 (FIGURE D), 43, 45, 60, 179
Diopside **38**, **140**, 141, 159, **160**, 162, **169**,
   171, 175, **176**, **178**
Dissociation 65–66
Dolomite **78**, 79, 81, **142**, 143, 144, 159
Dolostone 77, 79, 143, 144, 145, 160, 181
Dravite 166
Eclogite 38
Edenite 55, 171
Elbaite **47**, 49, 55
Elements 18, 19, 25, 56, 59, 61, 87, 89, 99,
   117, 123, 165
Elpidite 57, 59
Emerald 25, 46, 49. *See also* Beryl

Energy
    activation, in chemical reactions 106, 148, 149
    kinetic and potential 106
England, Cornwall and Devon 86, 88, 89, 124, 127, 130
Eosphorite **139**, 141
Epidote 95, **97**, 99, 171, 177
Equilibrium 105–107, 117, 147, 149, 156
Erythrite **132**
Euclase **42**
Eucryptite 137
Eudialyte 56, 57
Evaporite 24, 67, 77
Fault 16, 17 (FIGURE A), 67, 87, 181, 187
Feldspar 23, **32**, 32, 33, 43, 49, 50, 55, 56, 57, 111, 139, 159, 171
Fluor Silicic Edenite **169**
Fluorapatite 55, **86**, 89, 171, 172, **173**
Fluorine 33, 41, 45, 59, 86, 87, 89, 101, 169, 171
Fluorite **78**, 79, **89**, 95, 147
Forsterite 159
Franklinite 162, **163**
Galena **78**, 79, 89, 92, **122**, 123, 145, **162**, 186
Garnet 37, 38, 44, 45, 48, 49, 153, 171, 177
Garnierite 111
Geode 24, 81
Geothermal gradient 13–14
Germany-Czech Republic, Erzgebirge district 92
Gneiss 114, 159
Goethite **26**, 27, 73, 114, 116, **134**, 135
Gold **18**, 19, 25, 38, 75, 89, **90**, 91, 99, 123
Gossan 116
Granite 16, 17, 23, 24, 31, 42, 43, 43–55, 61, 75, 86, 89, 92, 114, 137, 139, 159, 165, 166, 185
Grossular 171, 175, **176**, 177, **178**
Groundwater 111, 114, 116, 119, 120, 123, 124, 127, 130, 147
Gummite 137, **138**, 139
Gypsum **66**, 67, 77, 100, 109, 111, 185, 191
Halite 25, **64**, 65, 67, 77, 107
Heat and pressure 24, 25, 27, 75, 153, 154–156, 157, 159, 160, 162, 165, 167, 177, 179, 180, 181, 185, 195
Hedenbergite 171
Heliodore 49
Hematite 73, 95, **96**, 97, 113, 114, 116
Hemimorphite 120, **121**, 123
Heterosite 137
Heulandite 85
Hiddenite 49
Hollandite 73
Holmquisite 166
Hutton, James 11
Hydration-dehydration reactions 109, 148
Hydrogen 89, 92
Hydrothermal solutions 24, 52, 74, 75, 81, 84, 85, 87, 89, 91, 92, 93, 95, 99, 100, 101, 175, 177, 179, 181, 186, 187

Hydroxides 114, 124
Hydroxlapatite 191, 192
Hydroxylherderite **139**, 141
Ilmenite 32, 35, 167
Ions 65, 67, 73, 77, 79, 81, 85, 87, 92, 99, 101, 105, 107, 110, 111, 122, 123, 124, 143, 148, 165, 191
Iron 16, 27, 33, 46, 55, 70, 73, 82, 85, 89, 91, 95, 99, 105, 113, 114, 123, 144, 157, 167, 171, 181, 184, 186, 189
Isotopes 13–14, 37, 38, 89, 92, 185, 191
Jordanite **98**
Kämmererite **99**
Kaolinite 157
Kermesite 135, **136**
Kimberlite **36**, 37, 38
Kunzite 49
Kyanite **20**, 21, **155**, 156, 157, 159
Labradorite 31, **32**
Lamproite 37, 38
Laurionite 191
Lava 11, 20, 24, 30, 31, 32, 77, 82, 84, 85 (FIGURE G). *See also* Magma
Lazulite 95
Lazurite **160**, 162
Lead 13, 77, 79, 81, 89, 100, 123, 124, 144, 191
Legrandite 124, **126**
Lepidolite 55
Leucite 31
Limestone 21, 24, 25, 41, 69, **70**, 77, 78, 81, 111, 119, 124, 144, 145, 153, 157, 159, 162, 167, 169, 171, 174, 179, 181, 185, 186, 189, 191
Liroconite 124, **127**
Lithiophylite 55, 139
Lithium 33, 35, 45, 46, 49, 55, 137, 165, 166
Ludlamite 137
Luxite 171
Lyell, Sir Charles 11
Magma 17, 19, 24, 25, 27, 30, 31, 32, 33, 34, 35, 37, 38, 39, 40, 41, 42, 43, 44, 45, 49, 52, 56, 59, 60, 61, 69, 74, 75, 84, 86, 87, 89, 91, 92, 99, 153, 154, 155, 165, 166, 167, 171, 174, 179, 181, 185, 186, 187, 193. *See also* Lava
Magnesite 144
Magnesium 16, 33, 38, 46, 81, 85, 99, 143, 157, 159, 162, 166, 181
Magnetite **35**, 39, 113, 114, 167, 171
Malachite **22**, 119, **120**, 123
Manganese 45, 46, 49, 55, 60, **70**, 71, 73, 162, 167, 194
Manganite 73
Mantle 12, 13, 14, 15, 16, 17, 31, 38, 39, 156, 186
Marble **98**, 114, 144, 153, 157, 167, 171, 174
Marine evaporite 67
Matrix 31, 172
Meionite **170**, 171
Mesolite **20**, 85
Meta-autunite 109

Metamorphic rock **20**, 21, 24 (FIGURE B), 25, 27, 93, 106, 141, 156, 159, 174
Metamorphism 159, 177
    contact 155, 165, 166 (FIGURE I), 180, 181
    regional 155
    retrograde 141
Metasyenite 179
Metatorbernite **108**, 109
Meteoric solution 24, 74, 75, 82, 84, 89, 92, 100, 193
Meteorite **12**, 13, 24, 105
Miarolitic cavity 43, 45, 50, 57, 60
Mica **20**, 33, 39, 43, 49, 52, 55, 56, 137, 141, 154, **158**, 159, 166, 171, 185
Michigan, Keweenaw Peninsula 101
Microcline 49, **50**, 137
Millerite **112**, 113
Mimetite **130**, 131, 132
Minerals
    defined 19
    indicator 155, 156
    primary 114, 117, 192
    secondary 114, 123, 124, 135, 136, 137, 191
Mississippi Valley Type (MVT) deposits 24, 77, 78, 79, 81, 101, 186
Molybdenite 52, **53**, 55
Monazite **54**
Monetite 191
Mordenite 82, 85
Morganite 49
Mudstone 95
Muscovite 52, 55
Namibia, Tsumebl 123, 124
Natrolite 57, 85
Nepheline 56, 57, 179
Nephrite jade 179
Neptunite **98**, 99
Neutralization 110, 111, 114, 124, 186
New Jersey, Franklin 162
New York, Sterling mine, Antwerp 113–114
Nickel 33, 88, 92, 111, 132
Nickel-Iron meteorite **12**, 13
Nickel-Skutterudite 88
Niobium 34, 39, 40, 42, 45, 56
Olivenite **124**
Olivine **12**, 13, 32, 33 (FIGURE C), 38, 39, 111, 141, 171, 175, 179
Ontario (Southeastern Ontario—Quebec area), Bancroft 167
Opal 25, 68, **69**, 195
Orthoclase 49, **97**
Oxidation 22, 24, 25, 113, 114, 117, 119, 122, 124, 131, 132, 135, 136, 137, 143, 148, 149, 185
    reduction reactions 113–116, 189
Oxide zone 114, 116, 119, 120, 123, 124, 129, 135, 148
Oxides 27, 34, 55, **70**, 71, 73, 82, 86, 89, 105
Paragenetic sequence 135–136
Pectolite 85, 177
Pegmatite 24, 42, 43–55, 56–60, 61, 87, 137, 139, 165, 166, 185